PIECES

of the

POSSIBLE

PIECES
of the
POSSIBLE

How to commit to change

ADRIAN KIRK

Matador
9 Priory Business Park,
Wistow Road, Kibworth Beauchamp,
Leicestershire. LE8 0RX
Tel: (+44) 116 279 2299
Fax: (+44) 116 279 2277
Email: books@troubador.co.uk
Web: www.troubador.co.uk/matador

ISBN 978 1783060 559

British Library Cataloguing in Publication Data.
A catalogue record for this book is available from the British Library.

Printed and bound in the UK by TJ International, Padstow, Cornwall
Typeset in 11pt Aldine401 BT Roman by Troubador Publishing Ltd, Leicester, UK

Matador is an imprint of Troubador Publishing Ltd

MIX
Paper from
responsible sources
FSC® C013056

This book has been several years in the writing, mainly because running a business has lead to it being side-lined. Also, the version you read here is the second version. It was initially written in what I refer to as a 'telling' style; where the reader was merely being told what to do. Having put it to one side for a year, when I came back to it I realised I wasn't a fan as a reader of this style; so I decided to create a story as a vehicle to convey the message. This added several years to the process and meant I needed to learn at least the basics of story-telling and character development. Along the evolution of this book I have received support and advice from many people; but most significantly from my good friend Anthony Hewson, who has been invaluable in steering me as a writer.

Preface

Thank you for picking up Pieces of the Possible, hopefully you've either read it or are considering reading it; maybe you're just flicking through wondering what it's about. Whatever your reason for reading this page let me explain why I wrote the book.

After many years of working with people to develop their presence and communication style in a corporate environment I realised there was a key area restricting them from becoming what they could be: and that was their willingness and commitment to create personal change. This was when I developed the Mindset Principle, which in essence gave me the impetus to write Pieces of the Possible. Put simply, The Mindset Principle states that our thoughts generate our behaviours and our behaviours create the outcomes we experience. How we think influences the experiences we have.

Pieces of the Possible is not written to hand hold you through practical application tips to creating change; moreover my aim is to empower you to choose what you want and commit to making it happen.

I believe the biggest step forward in making change happen is the decision to make it happen. Once we have decided we're going to make something happen we tend to do what it takes to make it happen. And that is why you will read the words 'choice' and 'choose' all the way through Pieces of the Possible; because it is entirely about what you choose.

Reading Pieces of the Possible may prove uncomfortable for some of you as you reflect on the choices you have made to date. Just as our main character, Tom, stays with his discomfort, I encourage you to stay with your discomfort; it is part of the journey to letting go of how things have been and enables you to open up new possibilities.

At the back of the book I have distilled the key principles as a quick reference guide for those of you who prefer overview descriptions.

Waking

Light pulls me from the depths of sleep, stirring me like a fluorescent bulb flickering to life. The inside of my eyelids dapple as a mosaic of white and orange hues permeate their membrane. I am so heavy with relaxation it reminds me of lounging on a beach with the sun caressing my face. Wallowing in the comfort of my snatched oblivion I inch towards consciousness; the longer I keep my eyes closed the longer I can maintain this blissful moment. But, not knowing where I am or what time it is, curiosity gets the better of me and I ease my eyes open. Immediately a bright light shoots in and blinds me. I turn away, raising my hand, closing my eyes tight to protect me from the glare. The light rebounds around my head, shocking me wide awake. A few seconds pass before the light in my head fades and I dare consider opening my eyes again. But I want to know where I am and what the light is. I use my hand as a shield as I open my eyes slowly, taking my time to get used to this invasion. The light is bright but I become more familiar with it and move my hand away hoping to see what the light is. There is nothing ahead of me but a bright white space. I look around but can't make anything out; there is nothing but whiteness surrounding me. Where am I?

A yawn stretches my mouth wide, juddering my body loose. I rub my eyes in an effort to focus them, hoping I'll find something to identify where I am; but I can make nothing out. I'm confused. What is this place? Suddenly a noise fills the air. It's so intense I wince from the pain in my head, my hands shielding my ears. It's the deafeningly clear sound of metal crushing and glass shattering: of a car crashing. The noise stops as quickly as it came. I am frozen, my hands up to protect me, just inches from my cowered head. I stare intently into the nothingness ahead of me, wondering what just happened; and then it comes to me. The accident! Instantly images flash before me. I'm driving through fog, ahead I see a cars brake lights shining back at me like red eyes. Trying to avoid a collision I steer sharply into the empty lane on my left, but everything happens so quickly I'm unable to complete the manoeuvre and can't avoid clipping the car in front. Everything spins; noises scream at me: the thud of metal hitting hollow metal, of breaking glass and rubber's attempt to maintain a grip on tarmac. I'm transfixed as I recall the details. The action stops; everything is still and silent; until out of the fog, two white beams bear down on me. There's a desperate screech of tyres as a car careers towards me trying to stop. The lights grow large and clear; I brace myself for the impact, raising my arms to cover my head as the car runs straight into the side of my car. The noise is the same intense sound of collision from a moment ago. Then, just as before, everything stops abruptly and I am left with my arms around my head, my body curled to one side, knees towards my chest. Once again, all around me is white. I stare into the space ahead. "Fuck!" My heart pounds as adrenalin courses through me. I'm shaking and disoriented.

I turn to look behind and see nothing but an expanse of white. Squinting, I try to make out the edges of the room I'm in, something to tell me where I am, but there are no shapes, lines or forms to be seen. There appear to be no walls and no ceiling. Perhaps I'm not in a room! To add to my confusion, there are no sounds either. I appear to be in a void of some kind. I look down, but instead of seeing whatever I am reclining on, there is nothing; I'm suspended. Confused, I check my body and see that I'm wearing what looks like white pyjamas. I scan my arms and legs trying to make sense of how I've come to be wearing this outfit. But no memory comes to fill the gap. I was in the car, the accident happened and now I'm in this strange place, wearing pyjamas. I wriggle my toes to see if I can move them, to check if I'm awake; they respond clumsily. I stare at my hands, moving from one to the other, turning each over, front then back. There are no marks or scratches. In fact, as I continue the scan of my body, there is no sign of injury at all; no bandages and no sign of blood. I am in one piece; everything moves as normal. My confusion deepens.

Questions compete for attention in my head. Where am I? If I was in an accident, how come I'm not hurt? Where is everybody? Does Louise know I'm here? Then it dawns on me what was happening just before the crash. I was talking to Pete Wilson about the Bahrain project. Actually, I had been bollocking him about the project. Because we were behind on our time-line I had to fly over to manage the situation in Bahrain this weekend, which meant I would miss my time with Emily. Then I remember the conversation with Louise and, as if tuning into that memory, images merge in my mind, drawing me in.

"I'm just about to take Emily to school; can't it wait 'til later?" Louise says down the telephone, expressing her frustration.

"Not really, I kind of need to speak to you now; it's important," I say.

"And so is getting Emily to school." I can hear she's already getting defensive.

"Yeah, I know, sorry; it won't take long." I lodge my mobile between my ear and shoulder, pick my keys up from the kitchen table, grab my briefcase and head for the door to leave for work. It's early, but if I leave now I may miss the rush hour traffic.

"Make it quick then. We're still doing breakfast; and I'm picking Joanne up on the way."

"Who's Joanne?" I ask, closing the door behind me. The freshness of the frosty morning snatches at my face. I hear a trace of a moan. "Joanne is Emily's friend. I give her a lift to school sometimes. Is that OK?" she says, already using that methodical, clipped voice of hers with me.

"Of course it's OK, why wouldn't it be OK?" Cold air chills my lungs as I stride across the lawn, crushing pinnacles of frozen white grass underfoot.

"Well! Come on, what is it? You said you'd be quick."

"OK. So, you know I'm supposed to have Emily this weekend?" By now I have remotely unlocked the car and, just as I'm reaching to open the back door, my foot slides away from me on the slippery surface of the concrete driveway. I reel backwards.

"What do you mean *supposed*! Tom..." Her voice intensifies around my name. "Don't do this to me..."

I try to find my balance, my feet struggling with the ice beneath. "Stay calm..." I say, hoping to stem the flow of what's building on the other end of the phone. It hasn't taken long for us to arrive at our usual position; Louise letting rip at me when all I'm doing is trying to explain something to her.

"Don't tell me to stay calm!" she barks down the line.

Finally I find my ground. "Oh come on Louise, I haven't said anything yet..." But she launches back at me as I open the back door to put my briefcase behind the driver's seat. "Yes you have. You've made it damned obvious you're not going to see her this weekend, again. What is it this time?"

"Bahrain."

"You are joking me?"

"No, no, I'm not joking. There's a problem on the project, they need me to go over," I say, sliding in behind the driving wheel and putting the key in the ignition.

"And Emily needs you *here*. She needs her father!"

"Yeah, I know. I'm sorry. I'll make it up to her." I press the 'start' button and am blasted with Led Zeppelin belting out 'Good Times, Bad Times'. I dart a hand out to switch off the stereo and make out Louise, "What the hell is that?"

"Sorry, I just started the car and the music kicked in."

"Typical! You can't even be bothered to stop and have this

conversation with me, can you? You are incapable of giving me or Emily any time."

"That's not fair," I say, putting the phone down as the cars hands-free kicks in. "I have to get into the office for a meeting to discuss Bahrain. I've only just found out about this, Louise; you're my first call."

"Gee thanks... Go on then, tell me how you'll make it up to her."

I slip the car into gear. "I'll come over and see her as soon as I get back and.... How about the weekend after? I could take her then." The wheels spin a little as they try to gain traction on the icy surface.

"So, you think you can just pop round here do you, just when it suits you? You think you can change weekends when it suits you? Yet again, you think everyone's going to fit in around you?"

"That's not what I'm saying."

"Sounds like it to me, Tom."

"Oh please, just try and understand my situation. You know this kind of thing's beyond my control."

"So you keep saying. This is how it *always* is with you though, isn't it? Someone shouts and *you* jump, without giving *any* consideration to me or Emily."

"Come on, Louise, that's not fair," I say, heading towards the motorway, hoping the traffic won't be too bad.

"Not fair! How dare you. How *dare* you say it's not fair? You have *no* idea what it's like for Emily when you do this."

"Yes I do."

"Go on then." There's a loaded expectancy to her tone.

"What?"

"Explain how you think she feels when you drop her at the last minute to fly off somewhere. Do you have *any* idea how much she looks forward to her visits with you?"

"Yes.....!" I hesitate. I must admit, being separated from Louise for just over a year now it's hard for me to spend quality time with Emily and really know how she is or what's going on with her.

"I knew it! You don't have a clue, do you?" Louise bellows down the phone.

"Give me a chance," I say, wanting to avoid the usual argument. I try to gather my thoughts, but I've just entered fog and have to focus much more on my driving.

"Just how many chances do you want, Tom? How many chances before Emily gives up on you as well?" Louise says, her voice breaking as she speaks.

"*She's* my daughter. She won't give up on me. You might, but *she* won't." My frustration seeps out. Louise knew exactly what she was taking on when she married me. After all I had met her when she worked for one of my clients, so she was fully aware of the nature of my work; she knew all about the pressures and strains. But, after Emily was born she changed and became much less understanding. Her assumption that Emily would give up on me just as she'd given up on our marriage irritated me and touched an already exposed nerve.

"God, you really live in another world don't you? Can't you see what you're doing to her? She loves you, yet you treat her like she's a number on one of your spreadsheets."

"Oh, come on!" My determination to hold my anger back gives way as my voice raises.

"No, *you* 'come on', Tom. You take her for granted, just like you took me for granted."

"I *never* took you for granted."

"Yes you did. You left me to do *everything*. You never thought about how *I* felt or about what *I* wanted. Or Emily! It was always what was important for you. You never *once* thought about how I was or what I might've wanted. Nothing's changed has it?"

"Oh I don't believe it; broken record time again is it?" Here we are back in the usual loop; me trying to explain the demands of my job while Louise simply wants to blame me and throw accusations. "Do we have to go over this again? I'm no different to how I've always been. Work's always been important to me, you know that. *You're* the one that changed."

"Of course I changed! I had a baby! *We* became a family. I needed *you* to change. I needed you to be *here*. I still do, Tom. You are Emily's father and you need to be here for her, before it's too late!"

"And what exactly does that mean?" I jump back in.

"Oh, work it out for yourself. She's eight years old. You're missing her growing up. And she's missing having a father."

"But I *am* her father, I *am* here for her. I just need to be away every now and then; you know I do. Look, I'll make it up to her. But I *have* to go to Bahrain this time. I'm the Project Manager on this one."

"Fine!" Her voice signals reluctance.

"So we're OK then? I'll take her the week after next? Is that OK?"

"No, Tom, it's not OK. I'll do it, but you've got to realise, this is not OK."

"Oh, Louise, please just give me a break. There's a lot of pressure on me with this project, the deadlines are tight and I'm running the risk of penalties kicking in if we don't finish on time. I could do without going over there to be honest, but I have to."

"You are her father, Tom; but you're not *being* her father. There is a difference," she says, sounding a little calmer. "Open your eyes and see what you have before it's too late; if only for Emily's sake."

Things had become so bad between us before we'd broken up that she'd been accusing me of being a poor father; even of being a bad influence on Emily. So while hearing her say this wasn't new to me, I still found it hurtful. But for now, I'd got what I wanted and thought it best to back out while the going was good. "Right. OK. Will do. I've got to go now, Louise, the lines breaking up. I'll try and speak to Emily before I leave. Bye." I end the call and look to check the road ahead. Seeing no cars, I pick up the phone again and dial Pete's number. It goes straight into a dead tone. The fog must be affecting the signal. I try again and manage to get a signal; the phone rings, Pete answers.

"Hi Tom."

"OK, so have you arranged my flights yet?"

"Give me a chance, we've only just agreed you're going over. As soon as Travel are in I'll get them to organise it. Look, Tom, I'm sorry about this; I just didn't foresee this glitch."

"This *glitch*, as you call it, means I have to be at a meeting that shouldn't be needed. You really should think ahead, Pete. If you'd fully planned your contingencies, we wouldn't be in this mess. I need to trust that I can leave things like this with you, I don't want to hand-hold the project, but if..." I stop because I hear the signal has dropped out. I pick up the phone to check the signal strength; there's one bar showing, so I press redial. The call connects, but the line is crackling badly. Pete answers; I can hardly make out what he is saying. The call drops out. This time there is no signal showing. I look up to check the road and I see the car with red eyes staring back at me through the fog. "Oh shit!" I drop the phone, grip the steering wheel and slam the brakes on hoping to stop in time, but realising I'm not going to I steer sharply to the left. The crash plays through just as before, at full pace, leaving me dazed in the void of whiteness and silence.

My heart pounds, my mind races, my stomach churns. I sit absolutely still, my eyes fixed ahead on nothing, trying to understand what's happening. Was there an accident? Is this real or am I dreaming? My senses slowly come back on line, calming from the shock of the crash. As my focus becomes clearer I look myself over again just to check I'm in one piece, and in doing so I'm reminded that nothing is actually supporting me. Immediately I feel unbalanced. My arms try to stabilise me as I look around trying to make sense of my predicament. What *is* this place?

It's very weird, but like finding my ground after stepping off a rollercoaster I gradually adjust to the idea of being suspended; shifting my weight one way then the other to find my balance. The initial fear of falling wanes and I pivot forward to an upright position. Tentatively I put my left leg out and down, and despite seeing nothing below me I can feel firmness under foot. Meeting enough resistance to suggest that something is taking my weight, I try my right foot. I take a step forward, my arms again rising sideways as though walking on a tightrope. Soon I realise I don't need to stabilise myself; I'm walking as normal. Perhaps if I explore this place I'll find something to give me a clue as to where I am. I walk warily, my feet landing on a non-existent floor. Yet wherever I venture there's nothing to be seen. Everything is the same; whiteness all around with no delineating features. I call out, "Hello!" My voice fills the air, and disappears. My eyes search around following my ears as they strain to hear anything come back, but nothing comes. No echo; no reply, nothing. "Hello!" I say again, only louder. The same; my voice cracks the silence momentarily and is then gone. No one replies. No noise comes back. A sense of isolation encroaches as the silence closes in around me. Feeling vulnerable in this chasm of emptiness, my body deflates backwards and, to my surprise, I find I'm cosseted as if a chair has come to meet me, accepting me as I recline into it. I cautiously tilt back, bewildered, but find myself comfortably supported. With hands resting in my lap, I look around assessing the situation. Where is everybody? Isn't someone going to come and see how I am? Surely I'm being monitored; I have, I think, just been in a serious accident. It seems I may have had a lucky escape.

Perhaps I'm in shock and having hallucinations. Is this what shock does to you?

Will I be able to make Bahrain? Pete might have to go in my

place. The project is resting on his shoulders now. As soon as I'm able I'll give him a call to talk through what's required.

I hope Louise will come to see me.

Images

As I contemplate my predicament, lost in my own world of confusion and questions, something distracts me. Where there had been white beneath me, I swear I can now make out a colour appearing. It's so subtle though that it takes all my attention to work out if it's real or in my imagination. As I stare between my legs bemused, the colour grows in intensity. Turning to look sideways, I see colour bleeding into the space around me. All my previous thoughts disappear, replaced with incredulity at what I am witnessing. What *is* happening? What is this place?

I watch as the colour takes form. All around me the space continues to grow darker, except directly ahead where a pillar of light remains. Then I see something that makes me peer intently forward; I'm sure there is an outline of people silhouetted in the pillar of light. It's difficult to make out who they are as my eyes adjust to the by now bright light beyond them. Suddenly the image taking shape makes sense. I am standing in the wings of a stage, facing out towards an auditorium. On the stage I make out a platform with several formally dressed people, sat behind a brightly lit long raised table covered with red baize. Between me and the stage are a couple of people who had earlier been silhouetted. They are in their early twenties, dressed in graduation gowns with mortar boards on their heads. Everything is now as clear and as real to me as if I were actually standing in the wings of the stage with those people. I peer forward again, in an almost double-take, as I make out a face I haven't seen in years. It's Niles, my friend from university and he's beaming his distinctive smile from ear to ear. The penny drops; this is *my* graduation ceremony! Beyond him the other person walks on to the stage, up to the raised table and as they turn, their graduation certificate in hand, there is the sound of rapturous applause. Not only am I watching events from sixteen years ago, I'm hearing the sounds as if I were living them again.

Just how is this happening? *Am* I dreaming? *Is* this an hallucination? This is *my* graduation for sure; *my* memory. It's as if I've gone back in time, it's so real. I can't believe what I'm experiencing. I'm filled with an immense sense of joy, twisted and mixed with confusion and fear. University was such a good time; everything spanned ahead of me, I aspired to so much and felt I could achieve anything I wanted. Seeing Niles takes me back to all the good times we'd shared; like when we'd get back home in the morning just in time to shower and make our first lecture, still drunk from the night before. He was a great character, the life and soul of just about every party going. I remember how pleased he was just to have been awarded a degree; the grade had been irrelevant to him. But seeing this playing out before me, in this strange place, quite frankly scares me. I flit between enjoying the reminiscence and fear over how and why this is happening.

Niles leans towards me and shouts, "Can you believe this?" His eyes alive; then turns to walk into the bright light of the stage. He marches proudly up to the platform, takes his certificate, shakes the Dean's hand and, in true Niles style, raises his certificate in the air, lifts his mortar board and throws it in the direction of the audience with a yelp of delight.

Seeing this play out so vividly fills me with the strangest sensations. I'm drawn in and fascinated by the wonder of this happy memory from my past, yet equally confused as to just how any of this can be. It reinforces that I really have no idea where I am or what is happening to me. I am now next in line to walk on stage and receive my certificate. My sense of bewilderment deepens as the perspective before me is that as seen through *my* eyes of sixteen years ago. Even though I stay sat, transfixed, it's as if I'm moving through the scene. How I moved and what I saw then is what I see now; it's as if a camera had shot the footage through my 21 year old eyes and is projecting it back now. As much as I'd like to stop this happening, to 'stop the ride and get off now please', I have no control. It actually looks as though *I* am walking out into the light and onto the platform.

As I move towards the platform the view changes, panning left to take in the audience, and I see something which takes my breath away. There, sitting three rows back, are my mum, dad and sister, smiling at me and clapping for all they're worth. It's amazing to see them all together. My dad alive. I can't help but smile as I watch them looking back at me with such pride and joy. They all look so healthy and, of course, younger. But my happiness turns into nostalgic sadness as I recall my dad's illness and how hard it has been for my mum these two years since he died. I struggle as my emotions jostle between extremes of joy, sadness and fear. The noise of applause is quite deafening as the scene turns back to the platform in time for me to be greeted by the Dean, who hands me a certificate and shakes the hand that is offered, *my* hand of sixteen years ago. I move along the line and shake the hand of my course tutor; a friendly but firm man who'd once severely reprimanded me for not handing assignments in on time, but who also gave me extra time to complete them. I turn to face the audience again and as I do the scene begins to pale, as if the colour has been unplugged and is seeping away. My graduation memory is fading; and as it does, I see my arm raising my certificate in the air as a salute to my family, and there's Jane, my sister, standing up to cheer as I walk off stage.

My thoughts turn inwards, as my emotions battle for attention. Seeing my family as they had been all those years ago has shaken me. I reflect on how things were and wish I could go back to those times; my dad alive, mum happier and me not facing the prospect of divorce. Everything's different now, somehow more complicated. The overriding feeling that surfaces is fear; of what or who is doing this to me, and how. I don't understand what's happening to me.

Am I in a dream? Or am I awake? I *feel* awake, yet this is weird enough to be a dream. Only in dreams do such things happen and only a dream could make sense of what I am seeing and experiencing. This can't be real. I sit back in my non-existent chair trying to understand, my mind sliding up and down a scale of memories, jumping between thoughts. I am completely alone in a space that appears limitless. Fear mingles with loneliness, I have no control and I don't like it.

My surroundings continue to fade, becoming lighter; but before turning completely white again, the colours start to gain depth once more. What's happening now? I watch the colour become clearer, like a photograph developing in a darkroom, forming a new image all about me. I make out a woman I don't recognise; she looks like she's a nurse, holding a door open for me to enter a room. Again, I'm watching a scene as if played out through my eyes and what I see next as everything becomes vividly clear has me in rapture. Ahead of me I see Louise, sitting in a hospital bed, bolstered upright by several pillows. I remember the scene so well: it's less than an hour after Emily was born. This is me walking into Louise's room, the midwife holding the door open as I carry my newborn child. Every part of me is focused on this life changing moment from eight years ago. Louise is looking radiantly tired, resting after a difficult fifteen-hour labour. Her face beams into life as she sees me coming in. The perspective changes, as I peer down into the bundle in my arms. Emily is wrapped in a yellow woollen blanket, her pink squashed-up face struggling to hold sleep at bay, a dainty, miniature hand randomly moving in front of her open mouth. This was undoubtedly the proudest moment of my life; holding Emily in my arms for the first time. The end of nine months waiting as she formed inside Louise. We'd made it through months of hospital visits and tests when there'd been complications along the way; but here in my arms was my first-born, my only child.

I walk towards Louise, lifting my eyes to look at her; her face glowing a smile back at me. What happens next is indelibly etched in my memory. The scene shows me leaning over to present Emily to Louise and in doing so I stumble on my own foot and end up banging my knee against the side of the mattress. Even though I know what's happening in this play back, I jump to my feet and dart my hands out in an effort to help the bumbling version of me save Emily. Louise's eyes and mouth shoot wide open as she sees me stumbling towards her, desperately holding on to Emily. Luckily the bed cushions my fall and I land sitting next to Louise's legs. Emily ends up in Louise's arms all right, but not as delicately as I had hoped, and by now she is, of course, crying.

The memory of this moment from my life engrosses me as I watch it playing out, uttering the words "I'm sorry" at exactly the same time I hear them spoken from my voice in the scene; which makes me smile. Then, just as before, everything starts to pale, as Louise looks down into Emily's face, her lips pursed forwards offering a reassuring 'Shhhhhh' to calm the tears.

Emotions take over again as I lose all sense of the sights now fading in front of me; the sounds and the faint smell of the hospital which had accompanied the projection of my life are gone. I am left deep in thought. There is no question, becoming a father was one of *the* most memorable and meaningful moments of my life; one that filled me with pride. But my emotions right now are almost too complicated to understand. Seeing that moment again I relive my pride, but at the same time an overwhelming sense of sadness expands inside me, taking over. This was one of the happiest days of my life; yet seeing Louise as she had been eight years ago, happy and in love, reminds me of how we are with each other now. Elation and sadness fight inside me, forming a ball fit to burst though my throat. What I have just seen reflects a time that no longer exists, a person who no longer exists; *me* with dreams, hopes, passions and desires. As I follow my thoughts down their path, I realise why I feel sad; it's a sense of loss of something that had once felt good, a feeling of lost possibilities. My mind starts to compare the *me* of then to the *me* of now. Sure, I have many things to be happy about: I have a good job, a very good job in fact, my house is OK, my car is, *was*, fantastic; I earn good money, travel the world and have a lovely daughter who means so much to me. But, there is no doubting it, Louise and I are going to be divorced; I see Emily every other weekend, when I can; I work long hours and my life seems to revolve around doing things that, I'm beginning to think, don't satisfy me anymore. My job certainly doesn't satisfy me the way it used to, yet I keep on working harder and harder, earning more money, meeting deadlines, attaining more status.

A thought surfaces, helping make sense of something I've been feeling of late, but which I've been suppressing; a feeling I now recognise as discontentment. Louise has never faltered from stressing that the reason she wants to leave me is how, as she sees it, my desire for more success at work has had an adverse effect on how I am with her and Emily at home. This never made sense to me, I never understood what she was talking about; but, with what's coming up for me now, I start to consider that maybe she's right. I have all the things I *thought* I wanted; but maybe they've come at the cost of things that, deep down, are fundamentally important to me. Things like happiness, love, family, excitement and passion. It dawns on me: am I complacently sitting on the conveyer belt that is my life? Have I been going through the motions day to day, merely ticking boxes?

My internal conversation has delved so deep I've become completely disconnected from what's happening around me. Another image has arrived, enveloping me and jolting me back into consciousness. I am in the middle of a scene from a mere two years ago; my father's funeral. By the time I am fully aware, the scene is as clear and real as if I were there now. What I see through my eyes of two years ago switches me onto another track on this rollercoaster of life experiences. I'd already been feeling sorry for myself, but this scene takes me to deeper sorrow as I watch the final moments of my father's time on earth. Before me is a chapel, with a coffin moving along rollers towards cream coloured curtains, slowly drawing apart. To the side of the curtains are vases with tall white lilies and vivid green foliage. The coffin is adorned with wreaths, one of which stands out among the mass of white and green. It's the wreath my mother had placed on the coffin, made entirely of red roses with lush dark green leaves. Around me I hear the music chosen by my father; he had requested that his final journey should be accompanied by Wagner's 'Ride of the Valkyries'. My father was a fan of classical music and opera, I think he'd chosen this piece not only because he loved it, but also because he knew people would laugh at the idea of him being transported to Valhalla by a bevy of buxom wenches. My head drops down as I exhale through my nose a hint of recognition at his last humorous gesture. Then I become aware of another sound sharing the chapel; the sound of my mother. She's on my right, leaning against me, crying her last farewell to the love of her life. I know this anyway, because I remember my father's funeral as if it were yesterday, but also because the perspective of the image changes as I turn to look at and embrace my mother. Tears streaming down her face, she can barely lift her head to watch my father's coffin disappear; but as she does, I hear her faintly whisper the words which had struck to the core of my heart in that moment two years ago and have stayed with me ever since, "Goodbye, my love." The coffin enters the space behind the two curtains and they slowly come back together, taking my father away from me one more time. With one precise movement the perspective of the scene shifts away from the images of curtains, flowers and my mother. I see the vaulted ceiling of the chapel, the colours of the exposed oak beams fading and blurring as a tear trickles down my cheek.

There is no doubting how important my father was to me, yet I'd never felt close enough to let him know that I loved him. He was an approachable enough man who knew many people and was well respected; yet he wasn't the sort of person it was ever easy to get close to. He was always kind and considerate, but he never expressed how he felt; he would often shrug off emotional conversation then find other things to do around the house. If I hugged him, he would give a flicker of a hug back and move away saying something like, 'That's enough of that nonsense'. He was a genuinely likeable man, cared for by many, who belonged to an array of social clubs, but his inability to express love had rubbed off on me. A new wave of sadness comes over me as I realise that I never actually said the words 'I love you' to my dad. My sadness sinks even lower as a new truth surfaces. I think I have learned to not express love in the important relationships of my life; including one of the most important: my marriage. Divorce from Louise is pretty much a foregone conclusion and so far I haven't allowed myself to acknowledge the sense of loss burgeoning inside me. A sense I've been keeping hidden away, unrevealed in a safe protected place. I have not allowed myself to be seen as vulnerable, in need of any help; I've been going through the motions of my separation and inevitable divorce without expressing emotion. The lump in my throat keeps growing, proving difficult to swallow, no matter how I try. Another tear runs down my cheek.

The scene fades further and further away until no trace is left and, once again, I am surrounded by white space. I wait expectantly for another scene from my life to appear, for a trace of colour to emerge again from the whiteness, but nothing comes.

I am left alone, trying to make sense of all that has happened, and is happening, to me. Bemused at what I've just experienced, my emotions struggle to stabilise. Then, ahead of me, I make out something against the white background; a small shade of darkness, moving. I wipe away the remaining tear from my eye and strain to see what it is. This is different to before, nothing is materialising around me. Whatever this is, it is in the distance and is getting larger, like it's coming towards me.

It's a person, walking slowly in my direction.

Gabriel

At last, someone to make sense of all this and answer my questions. I make out a man, wearing a white suit. Is he a doctor come to look me over? He is graceful and tall, of slim build, with a dark complexion and short black hair. Then I see that he's not wearing a suit but what look like the same white pyjamas I have on and that he too is barefoot. As he gets closer I can see he has the appearance of being mixed race, but I can't make out any particular origin. He's not distinctly male looking either, instead somewhat asexual. He has no defining features; no facial hair, no round hips or broad shoulders. He just looks, well, human.

I'm curious as to who this person is and what he has to say. Can he provide me with some answers? I move to sit more upright, ready to talk to him. But as I do, I catch his striking blue-grey eyes; looking straight at me. There is something about his manner, an inner state of stillness and peace; a sense of him being completely at ease with himself and with me for that matter. I usually arrive at a decision about the people I meet in seconds, but I struggle to form an opinion about this guy. I want to speak. I want to ask a question; but I'm stopped in my tracks. As I look into his eyes, any sense of uncertainty wanes as he holds me quite transfixed, exuding a reassuring calmness. His face is expressionless. He stops only a few feet away from me, offering a trace of a smile. "That was a nasty accident, Tom. How are you?" The warm tone of his voice matches his demeanour.

"So there *was* an accident then, I didn't dream it?" I reply.

"Yes, there was an accident. You should drive more carefully," he says wryly.

"Sorry!" I say, caught out by his approach. I have no idea who this guy is; who's he to say this to me? I'm confused and a bit on edge, "what do you mean?"

He dips his head slightly with a hint of a knowing smile. "Well, you did cause the accident," he says, raising his eyebrows ever so slightly.

"What! How do you mean? It was very foggy out there you know. Anyway, how would you know?"

"Oh there's a lot I know about you, Tom."

Something snaps inside me; after what I've just been through, this is too much. "Just who *are* you?" I get to my feet and look him in the eye.

He gives no sign of recognition that I've risen in challenge to him. "You can call me Gabriel."

We hold each others eyes as his name filters into my consciousness. "Thank you, Gabriel." His lack of reaction deflates the tension a little and my voice softens. "So, what do *you* know about the accident?

"Oh, I know a lot about you and the accident," he says, his trace of a smile returning.

"Sorry. You walk in, calm as you like and start this bizarre conversation, making everything sound completely normal when it plainly isn't. So, would you please tell me who you are and what's going on?" My words linger as he looks back at me without a single change of expression.

He holds the silence like it means nothing to him, as if time were irrelevant; just calmly looking back at me. "Perhaps you'd like to sit?"

"No thanks, I'm perfectly fine standing. Perhaps *you'd* like to answer my questions?" I say, not taking my eyes off his.

He blinks with the assured grace of someone unflustered. "I'm your guide."

"OK. Time out!" I raise my hands in surrender. It really hasn't taken long for this man to irritate me with his evasive and uncooperative manner. "Stop with the games now and just tell me… What's going on?

"Perhaps you'd like to take a seat?" he says again, this time gesturing behind me.

"Very funny." But to my surprise as I look round, a mauve fabric covered sofa has appeared where I'd previously been sitting. I turn back to face him. "How'd you do that?" I say, the wind somewhat taken out of my sails. "Please, just tell me what on Earth is going on here."

"Ah, now I'm afraid *that* poses a slight problem, Tom," he says, for the first time sounding somewhere near human as he does.

"What do you mean? How could *telling me what's going on* be a problem? It should be quite straightforward." My frustration jumps back.

"Because we are not *on* Earth."

"Sorry?" I'm not sure I've heard him properly.

"We're not on Earth."

"What? How can we *not* be on Earth?"

"Are you sure you won't take that seat?" he says gesturing with a tilt of his head.

"No," I say sharply. "What do you mean, we're not on Earth?"

He looks back at me, seeming to assess me before speaking. "It's easier if I just say that we are essentially in your mind."

If things were strange before, they just turned positively weird. Surely I *am* dreaming. "What are you talking about?" I demand.

He carries on, "You had an accident."

"Yeah, I think we've covered that one," I say sarcastically. "Go on. What do you mean, we're in my mind? Am I dreaming?"

"No, Tom; you are in a coma."

"A c…" The word catches in my throat; my lips frozen around the shape of the sound. I am shocked to my core, unable to speak. I stare back at Gabriel, not blinking, not breathing. Oh my god!

I'm in a coma! At least that, in some way, explains what's been happening to me. So this isn't a dream. I struggle with Gabriel's news. What does it mean? The accident must have been pretty bad then. What injuries do I have? Am I going to live or die? If this is me in a coma, what state am I actually in back in the real world? "Fuck!" The word quietly slips out. Is this it? Is this my life over?

Gabriel moves towards me, an arm coming around my shoulder as he does. "Please, sit down."

There is no resistance this time; I slump into the sofa. Thoughts teeter and fall through me one after the other.

Gabriel takes a step back, "Are you alright?"

"Er… Erm… I don't know." Time disappears from me as I stare into the whiteness beneath my feet, slumped on the sofa; everything is still. I try to make sense of my situation, but I can't think straight. Each thought fades before fully forming. Gradually I make out the steady beating of my heart. I am alive! Or so it feels. I am here in being, but surely not in body. My body is elsewhere, I can only presume in a hospital bed. Everything about what I feel here seems real; so, how can I be here, yet not be here?

"I'm sure you have many questions." His voice sounds like it's coming from far off, taking time to filter through; after a while his words form into a sentence in my head. I hear him but have no idea what to say or where to start.

"It's alright, Tom, whatever comes first. There's no rush," he says, bridging the silence like a hand of comfort and kindness. "This is your time."

"I don't understand *this*." I say, raising my head to look into the whiteness around me.

"That is hardly surprising," he says as he sits at the other end of the sofa. "It is very different from what you are used to. But you will acclimatise, in time; don't expect it to make sense straight away."

I turn to look at him. "But, how is this possible?"

"It's probably best if you try not to compare what happens here with what you are accustomed to."

"But..."

"Yes?" he says, probing for more.

"How?" I ask, finding only one word to express all my questions.

"Reality is in the eye of the beholder, Tom. Just because you haven't experienced this before doesn't mean it isn't possible," he says, offering a wry smile.

"Why me?"

"*You* brought yourself here, Tom. No one else."

"What?" I say, confused and frustrated.

"Your accident brought you here."

"How bad is it?" I ask, trying to fill some of the many blanks to my questions.

"Well, you are in a coma," he says, with a hint of sarcasm.

"Yes, but how bad is it for me? I mean, I don't appear to have any injuries," I say, looking down at my body again.

"As I said, Tom, don't expect to make sense of this straight away. Here you are fine; in the physical realm, however, your body is badly broken," he says. "But you are being cared for."

"Oh dear." My head drops. This really doesn't look good for me. "Is.... Does.... Er..... Does Louise know I'm here? I mean, does she know I've had an accident?"

"Yes, she does. She is at the hospital, by your bedside."

"Is she?" I ask in disbelief. Given how my relationship is with Louise I find it hard to believe she would want to be at my side. It's hard for me to come to terms with this news.

"Don't you believe me?" Gabriel asks, as if he knows what I'm thinking and is probing to draw me out.

"Oh, I don't know what to believe... I'm just surprised. It's just that we've been living apart for quite a while now, so her being by my side is unusual."

"Yes, but she is your wife?"

"In name only!" I say. "She wants a divorce."

"Does she?" he asks, with an almost disbelieving curiosity.

"Yup, she does…" I look ahead and exhale a sound of recognition at what comes up for me next. "You know, for a while I thought she'd met someone else. But apparently not; she just wants a divorce… She's going to make the application as soon as we've been apart two years. So, *that's* why I'm surprised she's at my bedside."

"People do the strangest things," he says, sounding like he's talking more to himself than me.

"What about Emily?"

"What about her?" he asks, chirpily bouncing back to be fully with me.

"Does *she* know about the accident?"

"No. Not yet. Louise's parents are going pick her up from school; they'll take her home with them and tell her later."

"And what about my mum and Jane, do they know?" They both live quite a distance from me. I'm sure my mum will be going spare by now if she knows about the accident.

"Yes, they've both been told. Of course your mother is worried; but Jane is making her way over to her now and then they'll travel to the hospital together." He speaks as if he knows everyone personally and is casually telling me at my bedside in the hospital.

"Oh, OK." I sit across the sofa from Gabriel, not knowing quite how to respond to everything he is telling me. Talking about my family coming to visit might just be bearable if I were conscious and discussing it with a doctor in hospital. But I am in a coma in a place that doesn't make sense, talking to someone who, I think, only exists in my mind. Someone who is sitting in front of me, responding to my questions and taking everything in his stride as if this were all quite normal. Then I realise that there are other important issues that need to be addressed. "I take it work knows then?"

"Yes, they do."

"And the..." But before I can finish, Gabriel interrupts; "Pete will be going to Bahrain in your place. There's *nothing* you can do, Tom. It is time for you to just *be here*." There is a decisive tone to his voice. "I'm sure you have more questions though. What else would you like to know?"

Not sure of quite how to respond to his manner I carry on, "Was anyone else hurt in the crash?"

"Yes," he says.

"Are they alive?" Panic hits me. The possibility I might be to blame for, or at least instrumental in, someone else's death is too much to take on top of everything else I have to contend with right now.

"Yes, they are alive. But their lives will never be the same. Each decision has a consequence, Tom; each action an outcome. I appreciate your concern for them, but driving the way you did, talking on your mobile phone, not concentrating and allowing your emotion to affect you, led to the accident. If you hadn't been on your phone, if you hadn't allowed your emotions to influence you, would you have avoided a collision? Would you be in a coma? Would these other people be in hospital?" He stops talking, letting his words settle. "It's time for you to take more responsibility for your actions, Tom. What you do can have far reaching consequences on other people. For example, the lives of those involved in the accident won't be the same."

It is a relief to hear that the other people involved in the crash are alive, but Gabriel's words cut through me. There is no doubting that he's telling me I caused the accident and that others are in hospital because of me. As much as I try to avoid this, playing his words back in my head, I can't deny it. Here I am in another, what? World? Dimension? Wherever or whatever this place is, I'm here because of an accident it seems I caused. This is too much for me to take in. I fall back in the sofa, struggling to come to terms with what he's telling me. But every time I get close to rationalising what I'm hearing my mind steers me away, wanting to avoid this version of events. Then my thoughts turn to the future. "What about me? How will *I* be affected?" I ask. "Will I live?"

"I cannot say. The fact that you are here does not mean you will live. I'm sorry to say that some who come here never go back."

Having gone slow before, time comes to a complete stand still on hearing this. Does he mean that I am going to die? I can't work out if he's saying that I might go back to live or I might not? Confusion jostles with panic as thoughts race through me. The images that came to me earlier are nothing compared to what's flashing by now; memories from my past flicker across my eyes: my first kiss, sex with Debbie Herbert, my first true love; my wedding day, sky diving, riding my motorbike. I try frantically to hold on to each one as it flits by; my heart beating faster and faster. The idea of death surges like a ball from my belly upwards and lodges uncomfortably in my throat; no matter how hard I try I can't swallow it. Is this really it? Is this the end? Will I ever get to see and feel, touch, taste, smell or hear again? Will I ever get to be *me* again? This can't be *it*! I haven't done yet. I don't want to die. I don't want to have it all end now. Not now. Not *ever* actually. But certainly not now. I'm not prepared. There are so many things still to be done. Crikey! I suddenly realise, there would be a funeral service. Who would choose the music for *my* funeral? As much as I'm engrossed in the experiences that are punching their way through me, I pull myself up to a standing position and stare Gabriel in the face. "There must be a mistake! I can't be dead. I haven't finished. I've still got things to do… Things to say… Places I haven't been to…" I catch my breath momentarily, moving away from Gabriel, pacing, looking for more words. Things I enjoy and will miss add to my despair: feeling sand between my toes, the sun on my face and the smell of earth on a fresh autumn day, a glass of chilled wine at the end of the day sitting in the garden, watching Emily play and laugh! Sadness at losing these things and more oozes in as I stand gazing into the void I see ahead of me. I try calming myself, maybe a humble approach will help. "OK, I'm sorry! To whoever I need to say it to, I'm sorry." I'm trying hard to keep tears from forming. "I'm sorry for all the mistakes I've made. I'm sorry… I'm sorry for…" Actually, I have no idea what I'm sorry for. My throat closes around words that won't form. Saying sorry seemed a possible answer; it takes me back to childhood, when saying 'sorry' was often the right thing to do. I'm grasping desperately at something, anything, to change what I'm feeling; pleading with Gabriel to stop doing this to me. Yet he keeps still, only his eyes move as they follow me. Facing away from Gabriel, my head hangs low having run out of pleas to offer. "I don't want to die." My words bracketed by the silence of the whiteness around us. "Help me, Gabriel." I lift my head again and turn to face him.

"There is nothing I can do, Tom. You are here as a result of your *own* doing. Whether you return is not in my hands," he says, his words landing softly.

In desperation I grasp at a moment of hope and lunge towards him, falling to my knees before him. "Whose hands am I in then? Who gets to decide?" I wait, hoping he'll give me the answer I need. But he just looks back at me in silence, giving nothing away. Doesn't he understand me? Doesn't he comprehend the full gravity of the situation? My mood turns to anger, as my emotions fight, trying to come to terms with this. It's not fair; I haven't had time to prepare. Surely I can be given a chance to go back. "You don't understand, I'm not finished. I shouldn't be here. This is all a mistake."

"There is no mistake, Tom. You are here because of your own actions," he says calmly. Unexpectedly, his face seems to express that 'It will be all right'. Even though I'm petrified of being where

I am, faced with the reality of death; just by being there, not saying anything, he is a strangely steadying influence. His silence and stillness speak more than anything I've ever encountered. Strands of what feel like invisible love emanate from him, enveloping and calming me, seeming to stroke me inside. I feel he is, somehow, taking care of me

"Can I at least influence whether I go back?" I enquire, somewhat numb with shock.

"I'm sorry; nothing you or I do can influence that." Even though there is a finality to his words, his tone is so neutral I feel he genuinely understands my plight and means no ill toward me.

I drop back onto my heels; desperately inquisitive for answers and hoping for certainties. "But if I don't go back, where do I go...? Do I stay here...? Can I at least know that?"

"If you don't go back, you'll go on to another place..."

"What other place?" I say, cutting him off mid-flow in need of more information

"That is not what we are here to talk about. That is not why *you* are here."

"Then why *am* I here?" I plead.

"You brought yourself here, Tom, remember that. Not everyone has the chance to come here. You are one of the lucky ones."

"Lucky?" I exclaim in astonishment, hoping my one word will express the scale of my disbelief at hearing this.

"Yes, lucky. Not everyone gets this chance to choose."

"To choose *what*?" My frustration jolts me back upright again.

"Why, to choose life being different," he says, his eyes widening almost imperceptibly.

"But I am happ..." I stop mid-sentence, staring into his crystal-like eyes. I had thought I was happy with my life; but, having witnessed the scenes from my life played back, I'm beginning to realise this hasn't actually been the case. Looking back at Gabriel I have a curious sense of lightness; a sense that it's all right to let go of pretence. It's as if he knows how I feel anyway; as if I am laid bare in front of him, being seen for who I truly am. Rather than be fearful of being seen as vulnerable, I have a sense of being at peace and safe. The all-encompassing white space seems to somehow feel less oppressive, even bordering on comforting, helping me feel at ease. I manage to swallow what is by now a much reduced lump in my throat. Gabriel continues to look at me with what can only be described as love. "Why now?" I ask.

"You came to me, Tom; it was *you* who chose this time," he says. "But for now, I think you should rest."

Before I can think of a response, all consciousness fades away.

A Place to Start

My eyelids part lazily as they do each morning; my mind taking its usual time to assimilate where I am and remember what happened before sleep. As everything comes into focus I see that I am somewhere other than my bedroom. It looks more like the library of a stately home. 'What the...' I wonder, 'What am I doing here?' I have no recollection of how I came to be sitting on this beaten-up leather Chesterfield sofa. To my side is a small table with an elegant brass lamp whose yellow light warms the surrounding space. Books line the walls to my left and right. In front of me is a large open fireplace with flames flickering in the hearth and, to either side, tall windows stretch from floor to ceiling, with deep red velvet curtains trailing along the olive coloured carpet. Through the windows I see green grass, leafy trees and blue sky. To the left of the fire place sits an imposing brown leather, winged armchair. Above the mantelpiece an intricate gilt mirror reflects yet more books back from behind me. As I gaze around I recall a dream of images from my life materialising to envelop me, of a car crash, of being in a coma and being visited by a man dressed in white telling me it's time for me to *choose*. I shrug it off as one of those dreams that stays with you when you wake, but it has left a strong impression in me that won't go; the images, the man and the car crash are as hauntingly real to me as the room I'm in now.

"Good morning, Tom!" comes a voice from behind me.

I turn sharply to see who it is, and there standing behind the sofa dressed in white, with a relaxed smiling face is the man from my dreams, Gabriel. It hadn't been a dream then? It had happened after all. His air of familiarity gives the impression he's known me for years. I watch as he moves around the sofa to stand in front of the armchair by the fire. "How are you today?" he asks chirpily.

"I thought you'd been a dream," I say; confusion, irritation and disappointment coming all at once.

"Oh, I am real." His eyes continue to smile at me as he sits in the armchair, the fire casting light across the side of his face. "How do you feel?"

"Confused," I reply, massaging my eyelids with my fingertips. "So it's all real then? I *am* in a coma?"

"Yes you are," he says, like he's reassuring me. "How are you? Are you rested?"

"I think so. But I'm still not sure where I am."

"There are other places beyond your reality, Tom. For now, relax in the knowledge that you are being cared for. No one is dead following the accident. You *are* in a coma and I am only able to be with you because you are in that coma." His voice offers a strangely calming tone.

"But what about Louise and Emily though? What about my family? How are they coping?" I enquire, hoping there's a way for me to see how things are or even send a message to let them know I am all right.

"It is understandable that you wish to know about others; but do not worry about them. Yes, people are concerned for you. Some are praying for you; some are even taking stock of their own lives following your accident. Remember, what you do has an effect on other people; your actions, what you say and do, have a ripple effect on them. But for now there is nothing you can do about them or the situation you are in, other than be here with me." There is a gentle firmness to his voice that offers comfort to my predicament and affords me a chance to reflect.

Being faced with the plight of losing the reality of life as I know it is the biggest 'time out' I've ever experienced. It feels like my life is on pause; as if I'm in a film that Gabriel has frozen, with me, as the main character, being allowed to keep moving through the stillness. I've stepped out of and am observing my life. Bizarrely, in being able to do this, I begin to see my life from a different perspective. I thought I had been *driving* where I was going, but, from this angle, I see that that isn't necessarily the case. Have I just been doing what I *believed* I should be doing? Maybe I've bought into following a way formed by society and the generations that came before me. I may have given the impression of being in control of my life, but have I merely been travelling along on autopilot, following a predetermined route?

"It is time for you to take stock of your life," Gabriel says, breaking my thought.

"Sorry?" I say, pulling my thoughts back to hear him. "What do you mean?"

"Well, for starters, how did you arrive here?"

I look at him through squinted eyes. "Surely I'm here because of the accident," I say, with a slightly quizzical tone, probing to see if this is the answer he is looking for.

He smiles. "It's certainly fair to say the accident led to you being here with me. That is correct; but my question is, how did you get to be this *version* of you?"

What a curious turn of phrase: 'this version of you'. Surely there is only one me. I try, but struggle with how to answer this question. Gabriel lets the silence be rather than fill it. Then I decide that honesty is the best policy. "I am me. I don't know any *other version* of me. What do you mean by that?"

"How did you get to be who you are, having what you have in your life?" he asks, making such a searching question seem extremely matter of fact.

I think of saying the first thing that comes to mind: surely I am who I am because I was born me. But is he asking something deeper? "I'm not really sure what you're asking of me," I say. "Many things have influenced me and led to me being who I am. But, this is me. I am who I am."

"And as such you are unique, Tom. Just as everyone is unique. You are unique because of your ancestry, because of your experiences and because of your choices. But everyone has the potential to be different versions of themselves. You could have been any of a number of different Toms. But everything you have encountered and experienced has led to you being *this* version of you right now. Every choice you have made, all the things you have said and done and all the things you have experienced have led to you being who you are, having what you have, right now. If you had done some things differently or had some different experiences; if you had made some different choices, you would be a different version of yourself. And the choices you made on the day of the accident directly led to you being here with me, to *this* version." He looks at me as if to let the idea settle. "Just as other people's lives can be affected by what you do, Tom, so *your* life and *your* experience of it are also affected. Each day you face a multitude of choices, just like everyone else. But the choices you've made so far have created *this* version of you. You all have the possibility of things being different. Indeed, everyone has the possibility of *being* different. The *choices* you make determine what you get back."

This isn't new to me as an idea, but being faced with the truth as glaringly as Gabriel is expressing it, given where I am at this time in my life, makes it that much more pertinent. My mind races through thought after thought, chasing along the history of my life, recognising the major decisions I'd made, and the paths they've taken me down. Then I think about events that have happened around me, events that have not been of my doing, over which I had no control. The fact that I fell into the sea and nearly drowned when I was six years old; that wasn't my fault, I was just a child. The school I had gone to, that wasn't my choice; it had been decided by my parents and the school system. My father's death;

death happens to everyone, it's not for me to determine when people die. "OK. I buy the idea of people creating *some* of what they have in their lives, but I can't buy the idea of people being responsible for *everything* in their lives. I haven't chosen everything in my life, especially when I was a child." I'm a little irate as I speak; the concept of asking people to take responsibility for everything in their life has always riled me a little.

"That is correct, Tom. But you did start making choices from an early age, and the sum of all those choices has led to you being you. You are right, some things have been beyond your influence, but *everything* you have experienced has played a part in creating who and how you are. All I have asked is, 'how did you get to be this version of you, having what you have in your life?' My purpose is to open your eyes. I am merely raising your awareness as to how you ended up being this version of you. Awareness is the first step to creating change. Nothing can be different if you are not first aware of how things are. Everything you have done and said, and all you have experienced, has led to you being who you are, having what you have. All the actions you take in your life reinforce this. If you are not aware of the part you play in creating your future you end up merely a passenger as life happens around you. And it *has* just been happening, hasn't it, Tom?"

He is so blunt that I find it difficult to respond, especially considering how much I've worked to get to where I have. But, given my reflections, it feels more true than not. "I guess it has," I admit, softly.

"Would you like to change that?"

I look into the flames of the fire, absorbing his words. I am in a coma, with no idea if I'm going to go back to live on. At the moment I'm struggling to come to terms with where I am, let alone know if I want things to be different. This is all a little too much for me. "That's really difficult to answer. This is hard to take on board. Surely it's hypothetical anyway? What point is there in talking about changing things? We don't even know if I'm going to come out of the coma."

"It could be hypothetical," he says, looking and sounding like this is a thought to be pondered. "But let's imagine, for a moment, that you *are* going to go back. Would you change anything?"

"Oh come on, Gabriel. You're playing with me. Are you trying to get my hopes up? I'm barely coming to terms with being in a coma and, *this*!" I say, indicating not just the library, but the magnitude of what the library represents. "Now you want me to speculate on what would happen if I could go back and carry on living!"

"I realise that this is hard for you, Tom. But..."

"Do you?" I interrupt, looking directly at him. "Do you have *any* idea of what this is like? It's like being buried alive; not knowing if I'll die or be rescued."

"Life is precious."

"Yes it is." The lump in my throat returns. "But it's only being faced with the possibility of losing it that I truly recognise that." I remember someone once asking me, if I had the chance to live my life again, would I do anything differently. At that point I had said 'No'. But being faced with the reality of it is a different matter altogether. Thinking about it further, when I was asked before, *that* was hypothetical; actually, *this* isn't. It couldn't get more real.

Seeing things as they are and feeling them as I am, my attitude adjusts. "I think... Given the chance... Yes... I would like certain things to be different." Gabriel listens passively, allowing the silence that follows. "Strange. It's only as I step off the ride that was my life, I... see it for what it is. Only by stopping life happening do I get this chance to assess it. To assess *me*." I look back into the fire. "You've put my life on pause haven't you?"

"No, Tom, *I* haven't put your life on pause. *You* have. You were the one who chose to drive your car while talking on a mobile phone. *That* is what caused the accident. *That* is why you are in a coma. Not everyone gets to pause their life like you have. Believe it or not, you are one of the lucky ones."

"Lucky!" I say, taken aback with his apparent disregard for my position.

"How you use your pause time will make a difference to how things play out *if* you go back. It's all about how you use the time you have created, the choices you make here in your pause time. Things can be different, Tom. But you must *choose* for them to be different. If you want change, if you want something about your life to be different, or to have a different experience of life, you must choose to look at life differently. You must respond to what you experience differently. If you *think* differently, Tom, you create the *possibility* of a different outcome."

"It's all well and good *wanting* things to be different," I say, rubbing my eyes again, my resistance to his ideas coming back. "But some things are just too far down the line to change. Some things *are* what they are, Gabriel. Some things are so well ingrained, too deeply rooted to change now. Let's face it, I'm quite set in my ways, I'm used to being me. There are things I do that I don't even think about, I just do them, they're habits..." I pause, remembering something. "Actually, someone I knew once described them as 'default behaviours'; things we do without even thinking: patterns, comfort zones. How can I change things like that? How can I change what I'm not even aware of?"

"You're right; it is difficult to change something you're not aware of. But to confine certain behaviours as habit and box them off as impossible to change is like being blind to the possibility of how things *could* be. Becoming aware is fundamental to change, and that's why we're talking about it. If you allow yourself to live from day to day, disconnected from what is happening to you, disconnected from how you experience life and from your own behaviours, then your experience of life will not change." He beats out the last few words to reinforce them. "If you believe that certain things can't change, then you will be proven right. And that is why this is a useful conversation for us to have, Tom. Maybe it's time to become more aware of these 'default behaviours', as you call them. If they are allowed to happen without being looked at, without light being shone on them, they will keep happening. A child who behaves badly and is ignored or not encouraged to behave differently will continue to behave badly. The good news though, is that you at least seem to have a degree of awareness around some of your behaviours. But, if you want to create a change, you must become aware of the behaviours that are reinforcing who you are, having what you have. Even the ones you say are just part of who you are and even the ones you say you have no control over."

"But that's what I'm saying. If I have no control over certain things, how can I change them?" I'm getting frustrated at repeating myself.

"I agree; if you have no control over something it is difficult to change. But there is something you *can* change, and that is your response to it. Perhaps I should be more specific?"

"Please do, because you're confusing me," I say, leaning forward in the sofa, hoping that he will make this simpler to understand.

He carries on. "This is not about changing everything, but about becoming aware of what you *can* and *cannot* influence; then making choices around these things. If you are happy with who and how you are, that is fine. But if you find yourself here…" he gestures outwards, "with time to look at your life and how you approach it, and you recognise something that you'd like to, and can, change, then why not do so? The conversations we have are designed to give you that chance. I'm talking about becoming more aware of how you are and the choices you make. About how you respond to the things that happen around you and which influence you. We are talking about tuning in to what you are doing: tuning in to how you are, to how you behave, how you respond; about becoming more aware of these things. Without awareness nothing can change. Most of what you do and how you respond *can* be changed though. It all depends on whether you want to change; how strong your desire for change is."

"I'm not sure how strong my desire is," I admit, recognising that it's one thing talking about the possibility of change but another thing altogether to actually want to make the change happen.

"Desire is what creates the momentum for change. It's the energy that helps fuel the journey of change. If you lack desire you haven't truly chosen to create change. But that is up to you, Tom. I am not asking you to commit to anything, other than being open to the ideas I offer you in our time together. After all, it was *you* who created this pause time," he says with a cheeky smile. "Are you thirsty?"

I fall back into the sofa with a gasp of disbelief. "You keep doing that, don't you?" Before he can reply I carry on. "You draw me into a conversation and then twist and change the subject altogether."

For the first time I see him shed his composed demeanour and show a hint of a hidden playful child. "That is the beauty of change; it can happen in any moment. As soon as you choose it, you open up the possibility of it. Would you like a drink?"

"Of what?" I ask.

"Anything. What would you like?"

Now that it's on offer, I realise how parched I am. "I'll just have a glass of water please."

Without a blink of an eye Gabriel nods his head towards the table at my side. I turn to look and there, beneath the lamp shade, is a tall glass of water. "How did you that?" I say, looking back at him.

"Things are different here," he replies.

"But how..?"

"Don't concern yourself with the how. Remember, you are in a coma."

"Yeah, thanks for reminding me!" I say, leaning over to pick the glass up. The water is refreshingly cool and soothes me as I sit back. "Thank you." I say, acknowledging just how thirsty I'd been feeling.

"It's my pleasure. Remember, Tom, I have not done this to you. My purpose is merely to guide you along a journey which will give you the opportunity to create change, should you wish it. I demand nothing of you, but your attention and a willingness to explore ideas with me. Allow these ideas time to settle. You do, after all, have time to give," he says, landing his comment with the certainty of someone assured in what they're saying. "One thing is for certain though, you will leave here. When that will be I cannot say, because I don't know; but leave you will. For now," he leans back in his chair, speaking with a lighter note, "you are here with me, so can I suggest we make the best of the time we have?"

There is something altogether final in what he has just said that leaves me quite cold. But he has, at least, left me with a trace of something to pick up on. I take another sip of water, place the glass back on the table and bring my legs up under me on the sofa. "I'm curious; tell me about wherever else I might go; if I don't go back," I ask, hoping to find out whether there really is life after death.

He looks at me for a moment, then blinks his eyes slowly. "We are not here to talk about other places. If you are going to go to another place, then I shall talk to you about it at *that* time. But for now, you are here, with me," he says, in his usual calm yet irritating manner.

What sort of response is that? It's amazing how quickly he has a tendency to irritate me. One moment he seems helpful and friendly, the next slippery and evasive. But in not answering my question, he raises another. "Come on, you must have an idea of when I'll leave you. You seem in control of most things, surely you know this?"

"You will know when you know. The future is created moment by moment. What you may think your future is going to be, won't necessarily turn out to be reality. Your actions and responses to what you experience influence your future. And some things just happen in the moment, don't they? Like a car crash." He pauses for a moment as I register that his voice has no sound of judgement whatsoever, before carrying on. "You can't plan for them. What is important is how you accept and respond to them."

I let out a sigh of frustration and look back into the fire dancing seductively in front of me, thinking about what he's just said. "But some things are foregone conclusions aren't they? Take my divorce for example," I say, turning to look straight at Gabriel. "That's a foregone conclusion."

"Is it?" he replies.

"Yes." The word leaps from my mouth. I take a deep breath in and carry on with a slightly more subdued voice. "I'm pretty sure my marriage is over. Louise wants a divorce. It's a done deal."

"Is it, Tom?"

"Yes." I repeat with no hesitation and complete resignation to the fact.

"Is that what you want?"

He catches me out with what is actually a very good question; one that starts me thinking. For the first time I feel I can be honest about how things are with Louise. This is, after all, *my* pause time, and Gabriel seems the best person, actually the only person, for me to be honest with. Being given the opportunity to step outside of my life and observe it gives me the chance to assess how I feel. I keep hold of his eyes as he allows me to follow a train of thought I've never really let myself have before: how I truly feel about my divorce. I listen and, from the pit of my stomach, a sense of relief emerges like a seedling slowly unfurling from soil, and works its way up until it sits in the back of my throat. I consider suppressing the words forming in my mouth, but they are intent on escape. "No, I don't think I do."

"There you go. That which you believed to be a foregone conclusion in your future, is not." He seems to be trying to lift my spirits.

"Yes it is, Gabriel," I say, a dejected tone signalling unshakable acceptance of the situation. "My marriage has broken down irrevocably; we have drifted apart. It's too late."

"No it isn't," he says, catching me out with his matter of fact tone.

I look up into his blue eyes curiously. "Are you telling me my marriage isn't actually over?" I ask, my spirits lifting slightly.

"I cannot make decisions for you and I cannot change how things are. You must do all of that yourself. Would you agree, though, that at this present moment, while things don't look or feel good for you, your marriage isn't actually over, is it?"

"Well, no, it hasn't actually ended yet; in that respect you're right. But all the signs are that it's over," I say, perplexed at his apparent naivety.

"There you are," he says, sounding like he's pleased that the penny has dropped for me. "Right now, it isn't over. Your projection about it being over is just that, it's a future focused belief. And, remember, the future is created by the choices you make moment to moment. All I am saying is that your marriage is not over right now. If you choose to, it is possible that you could change how you approach the situation you are in. You could change how you are in relation to your marriage with Louise; how you behave. The question is, Tom, how willing are you to change your approach? And how open are you to the possibility of *that* change creating a different outcome? Is it really a done deal, as you call it?"

"Hypothetically, you're right, Gabriel; but when two people have decided to divorce it's because they don't want to be together anymore."

"That is only the case because that's how you are choosing to look at, Tom. The whole point of being hypothetical is to introduce a different perspective and open up the possibility of things being different. The extent to which you are willing to accept that possibility determines the validity of that which you call hypothetical," he says, checking to see if I'm still with him. "The extent to which you are willing to engage with new possibilities influences what you create in your life. The extent to which you live your life passively or actively makes a difference. Does life *happen* to you, or do *you* influence what happens?"

"So, are you saying that, if I go back, I should save my marriage?"

He raises his eyebrows with a hint of a smile. "I'm merely raising your awareness around how you are with your life. It's not for me to determine what you do with your life; that is for you to decide. If you choose to change, that's up to you, it's your decision. I am only responding to you stating that divorce is a foregone conclusion. Sometimes, it is down to perspective. From where *I'm* sitting, it's not over. However, if you have made your mind up that it's over, then it probably is over. That's awareness. Be more *aware* of how you think in relation to what you experience. Everyone is capable of looking at situations from a different perspective. The question is, are you *willing* to look at it from a different perspective? Sometimes you might defend what you believe because you think you have something to lose by changing your mind."

I look across at him bemused by what he's just said.

"What are you afraid of losing, Tom? Respect? Image? Status? Power? What is it? Are you afraid of being seen as someone who changes his mind?" He looks back at me, delving in and challenging me. "There are many things that influence people. Many things stop them from changing their mind. Usually what they perceive to be important."

There is something quite unnerving about how he has this knack of accurately summing up my thoughts and feelings. All right, so these things aren't the be all and end all for me, but they certainly have meaning. I *am* concerned at how others perceive me; so what they might think if I change my mind matters and does influence me. As I think about this, he carries on. "But sometimes it's quite simply because people are not *aware* of a different perspective, or that they are not open to *seeing* it from a different perspective. Which is it for you? Are you aware of a different perspective in relation to your marriage? Are you open to another possibility? Or do you have something to lose? And if you have something to lose, what is it you have to lose?"

"Crikey! You don't hold back do you? Give me a chance, Gabriel; just when I think I understand what you're saying, you throw something new at me... OK, so... am I aware of a different perspective..? No, I *wasn't* aware of a different perspective; until you pointed it out to me, that is. As far as I've been concerned it *was* over. But I guess you're right, it's not over until it's over. Sorry, what was the next question?"

"Are you open to the possibility of what could happen if you look at it from a different perspective?"

"Jeez, that's a big one!" I consider the implications of doing just that. "Well, I guess if I look at it differently, my marriage may not be over. I suppose there's the possibility that Louise and I could try to make it work. But, Gabriel, there are lots of reasons why our marriage wasn't working."

"So, there is a possibility that you could stay in your marriage? Is that what you are saying?"

"Well... Yeees." As much as I have a trace of excitement at this 'new possibility', it's not easy just to dive in and be enthusiastic. I had been resigned to the idea of my marriage being over, especially given how Louise has been with me of late, so to lift my emotions into a new place is hard. "I do see it from your side, Gabriel; it's not *actually* over just yet. But as I say there are lots of reasons why it isn't working."

"If you change your perspective on why the marriage isn't working, if you change how *you* are in your marriage; if you choose to be a different version of you, in the marriage as well as in your life, could it work?"

Here he goes again. "It's all well and good talking about *me* changing, but what about Louise? It takes two you know?"

"Does it? Just as a dropped pebble creates ripples in water, so your actions radiate and have an effect on others. So, if you alter how you are, then you increase the likelihood of others responding differently to you."

"Are you saying if *I* change, Louise will change?" I ask, hoping he'll come back positively.

"Oh, there aren't any guarantees. But a change on your side at least opens up the possibility of Louise responding differently. So, what would you have to lose by being different, Tom?"

He hits the nail on the head, again. I do work long hours and spend a lot of time away from home. Having this conversation, now I can see how Louise might've thought I was taking her for granted. Looking back, although I certainly didn't intend to be that way at the time, maybe I didn't value our marriage enough. With this new perspective I see the part I may have contributed to my marriage breaking down. Gabriel's right; if things carry on as they have been, the foregone conclusion I've been talking about would undoubtedly be reached. Would I have anything to lose? Well, given that I already believed my marriage to be over, surely I haven't much to lose, in terms of outcome anyway. But, in order to save my marriage I would have to be *very* different. I would have to be a different version of me. Good grief; now I'm even thinking like him. But in becoming a different version, what would *I* have to lose? Well, initially I'd have to eat a lot of humble pie; I'd have to listen to and take on board what came back at me, notably from Louise. I'd have to change how I approach my work. I might even have to *change* my work! I look up at Gabriel. "I suppose it depends on what you mean by *lose*, doesn't it?"

"I think it depends on what is important to you," he says. "Is being 'right' important to you? Or are you willing to be humble in seeing someone else's perspective? It all depends on how attached to your way of doing things you are. Are you willing to change how you are in your marriage? Are you willing to change how you approach work?

"It depends how you think, Tom. If you think differently about *who* you are and *how* you live your life, you open up the possibility of things being different. My question is; how far are you willing to go? Are you *willing* to change?" he says, leaving the words to linger as he looks across at me. "If you think your job is more important than your marriage, then you will likely forsake your marriage. So I repeat the question, what have you got to lose, Tom? Are you willing to step outside of your limiting beliefs and discover new possibilities?"

"Crikey, you don't make it easy, do you?" This is beginning to feel like an emotional boxing ring. Gabriel knows how to land a punch and he's not taking his eye off where he wants to go with me.

"All I'm doing is giving you the chance to see things from a different perspective. What you do with that perspective is entirely your choice. But let me add this, what has being the way you have been up until now given you? Look around you. Where are you?"

I try to come up with an answer, but all I can think is that I don't actually know where I am.

"This library only exists inside your mind. You are actually in a hospital bed, in a coma, and you have no idea whether you are going to be given the chance to carry on living," he has me against the ropes. "So what do you have to lose, Tom?"

Forget what I've got to lose in regards to my marriage; I'm more concerned about whether I'm going to live or not. "Oh, come on, Gabriel," I plead, lunging forward, hoping he's going to relent and give in. "Is there any way I *might* be given a second chance?"

"I'm sorry, Tom, I cannot influence that," his tone mellows as he endeavours to offer some comfort. "As far as a second chance is concerned, who do you think will give you that?" He looks at me inquisitively with raised eyebrows. "*You* are the best person to give yourself a second chance. You could have started afresh any time."

"But I didn't know then what I know now," I say in frustration.

"That is why you are one of the lucky ones."

"Oh, don't start with that again. Believe me, it doesn't *feel* lucky." I rise from the sofa and walk over to the window nearest me; looking out I see a stone terrace leading to a beautifully manicured lawn stretching towards an array of mature trees.

Gabriel comes to join me, looking out of the window. "Like most people, you never realised what you had at your disposal, because you weren't aware. I'm just helping you to become aware. What you do with your awareness is your choice"

"OK, so, *if* I go back, I could try things differently, see what happens," I say, turning towards Gabriel. "But it's not all down to me; there are two of us in the marriage."

"You can at least take responsibility for your part, Tom. After all, it is you here with me, not Louise. It's *you* we're talking about. Everything you have experienced to date in your life, all you have done and said, has led you to *this* point. Your way of being has created everything you have in your life and the way your life is. If you get to go back and you carry on as you were, without change, it will only serve to reinforce the way things were."

"But does that mean *I'd* have to do all the changing?"

"Oh, you'll be surprised how much those around you change when they experience you being different. Your change in behaviour radiates out and influences others. But, let us take one step at a time." He walks back to his chair. "It could be anyone here with me," he says, with a lighter, fresher energy as he sinks back into his comfortable position by the fire. "But it happens to be you. Therefore, what is pertinent in your life will undoubtedly form part of what we talk about."

Again, he has caught me out. I wonder where he's manoeuvring the conversation to this time. "Go on," I say, returning to the sofa.

"Whatever is important to you will surface and steer our conversation. Understandably, your marriage is preying on your mind at the moment, so *that* is what we are discussing. But it is not what I am here to talk to you about."

"Sorry, I'm confused."

"Ultimately this conversation is about awareness, Tom. Because your marriage has such relevance for you at the moment, you brought it into the conversation and as a result, for you, the conversation has become about your marriage. Actually, talking about your marriage has helped to reinforce the very idea of awareness. By applying a new level of awareness to your marriage situation, you allowed yourself to see it from a different perspective; and *that* is what has released the possibility of a different outcome. It was the conversation on awareness that triggered that new possibility."

"So, my marriage could be different?"

"As I've already said, that's for you to decide. Now that you are aware of a new possibility, yes it could be different. But it's entirely down to you."

"So it's *down to me again*, is it?" I throw my head back in frustration.

"That's my point, Tom. It's *all* down to you. You are the only one here with me. Because you've steered the conversation onto the topic of your divorce, that is powering your understanding and you keep drawing us back to it. And because these ideas are uncomfortable for you to take on board you're looking for ways to escape it being about you, to avoid hearing what I'm saying, and you keep wanting to talk about other people. *Any* subject could be steering this conversation, the focus from me would still be the same. It's about to the *choices* you make. It depends on how you use the knowledge I give you," he comes forward in his chair. "It depends on whether you *choose* to make changes, if you *choose* for things to be different."

I feel bombarded with all he is giving me and asking me to take on board, given my predicament. "Yes, but how can I choose it being different if I don't know if I'm going back to live or not?" I lean forward, closing the gap between us, my frustration building at the fact that we've come back to the same stumbling block.

"People do come out of comas, Tom; you know that as well as I do, so there is a possibility you could go back," he says. "And, given there is that possibility, wouldn't you at least like to be prepared? You could choose to do things differently, to *be* different. You could take a more active part in influencing what happens as your life unfolds before you."

"But how will I know what is the right thing to do? I could make mistakes."

"Ooh, so you think there is only right or wrong? And that wrong means you made a mistake?" he says, pondering the words as he says them. "That is quite judgemental. There is no *perfect* way you know. You are all different and each of you behaves differently when faced with different possibilities. If what you choose turns out to give you something other than what you were hoping for, then rather than see it as a mistake, see it as a chance to try something new, to choose something different. Look, no one else can decide these things for you. But your level of awareness influences the possibilities that unfold before you. What you choose is up to you."

"But if I go back and do things differently, there's still Louise. She'd have to make some changes too."

"It is time for you to stop talking like this, Tom," he says, with a sterner tone. "Nothing will change if you carry on with this perspective. You cannot change Louise. But, she may choose to change if she sees *you* being different," he say's with a teasing hint of hope.

"But does that mean things will get easier between us?"

"So now you want things to be *easy*!" he says, mixing tones of disbelief and ridicule. "Who can tell how it's going to be? The future is created by the choices made moment to moment; and *that* brings us back to the broader idea of awareness."

"Does it?" I say, confused again. First he gets my hopes up about Louise, then he reprimands me and now I'm totally unsure where we are.

"Even though some things may be beyond your control, many things are within it. If your ignore how you have previously interacted with your life, then you will continue to be a passive passenger, reinforcing your current situation.

"However, by becoming more *aware* of how you are and the choices you make, you take the first step to altering how things *can* be for you. If there is something you don't like in your life you must choose to respond differently to it. Fundamental to the principle of awareness is becoming *aware* of how you respond in those moments of choice. Whatever you encounter, whatever you perceive, you can *choose* how to respond. Only awareness allows you to recognise the choices you have in those moments. And in *those* moments, you create the possibility of change.

"I am confident that you are responding to certain aspects of your life unconsciously though, Tom. You are merely responding out of these default behaviours and some of them are repetitive; so much so, in fact, that they have become automatic. The question is, how *aware* of these behaviours are you?"

By this time I'm feeling numb. He has certainly given me a lot to think about. OK, so it appears I have been somewhat unconscious of how I involved myself with my life; I recognise that now. But that's simply because I was unaware of an alternative perspective. I can't be blamed for this. As much as there's a logic to his ideas, I resist and resent the assumption that I should have known about them. "Are you suggesting that I am to blame for how my life is?" I ask.

"I'm not talking the language of *blame*. No one can blame you for not being aware. As I say, awareness is the first step. Recognising a lack of awareness around behaviours to date isn't a sign of weakness. Such moments of recognition are powerful in altering how things have been. They are key to setting change in motion; they're a fundamental step in the right direction. You have been among the many who live their lives unaware; and that is fine, no one is judged for being unaware. What's that saying, 'ignorance is bliss'?"

I can't believe I'm hearing this. An incredulous laugh slips out. "OK, so now I'm *ignorant* as well!" I say getting to my feet, his implicit assumption irritating me. I grab the glass of water from the side table and take a drink, trying to make sense of my emotions: disbelief at being blamed, frustration at my predicament, anger at feeling impotent, indignation at Gabriel's assumptions and audacious approach. I walk across to the fire and see myself reflected back in the mirror above for the first time since waking in the coma. It's still me, nothing different. The same eyes, the same hair, nose, mouth. It's certainly me looking back. I see the same person who looked back at me when I shaved in the mirror, what? Yesterday? Today? I see no marks, no scars, no injuries, nothing to indicate how I might be looking for real in a hospital bed, recovering from a car crash.

I place the glass on the mantelpiece and drop my head with a sigh.

"Now, Tom, don't go down that route. Ignorance is merely another way of expressing being *unaware*. If you accept that you have been unaware of this until now, then that means you are moving forward.

"You seem reluctant to take some of this on board; perhaps fear is stopping you from accepting all I offer?"

"I don't know what I'm feeling right now," I say.

"It is fine for you to feel this way; don't worry. But let me assure you..." he pauses, waiting for me to look back at him. "Resting between the dream of doing and the fear of failure lie the pieces of the possible. Don't allow fear to get in the way of discovering new possibilities."

I lift my head to look at him.

"So, I come back to my question; how much do you have to lose? If you accept that you have been unaware, if you accept that your responses and behaviours to date have created the reality of your life as it stands, then you are actually moving forward. Awareness is the first step. Acceptance is the second!"

"Acceptance?" I ask.

"Yes. Acceptance of the way it is."

"I know I'm supposed to be following all of this Gabriel, and I *am* getting some of it," I say. "But help me out a bit here; the way *what* is?"

"Don't be too hard on yourself or expect this to all fall into place easily. This is, after all, new to you. Whoever steered you in this direction before?" he asks, teasing a reply he knows isn't going to come. "No one! I know, because I know a lot about you. But not everything; I don't know, for example, how much of this you'll take on board and I don't know if you'll choose to make changes as a result of spending time with me. We've already established that I don't know whether you'll go back. So maybe you could just be a little easier on yourself? It is completely all right for you to question me and what I say. Go ahead, question, disagree, challenge me; I enjoy a good debate, it shows you're engaging with what we're discussing.

"So, to answer your question, acceptance means accepting that your actions, your behaviours and your responses to date, have created your life being the way it is. Being aware is one thing; accepting your part in creating how life is for you is another. There is good news though. It's never easy coming to terms with accepting your part in creating things as they are for the first time, but once you are over that initial obstacle, it does get easier.

"You are actually at one of the most difficult stages in your journey with me, Tom. How are you feeling?"

"I feel pretty bloody lousy actually. And confused," I admit.

He smiles. "What you feel is normal; even natural. As I say, who has ever talked to you about this before? Who has ever challenged your way of being before?" He looks at me, dipping his head down, slightly tilting it as he does so, and raises his eye brows with a knowing look denoting 'I'm right aren't I? No one ever has'.

I sigh a sigh of recognition in accepting that he is right and as I turn my head towards the large window by my side I see the sun shining in a beautiful clear blue sky. Encouraged by the appeal of a world I recognise and miss, I turn to face the window fully and gaze at the lichen-speckled terrace and the lawn beyond. I'd like to feel the warmth of the sun on my face again and a gentle breeze against my skin. "People don't talk to each other like this though, do they, Gabriel?" I say. "So, yes, you're right, no one has ever talked to me about awareness and acceptance."

"No, but these ideas are not new, they have always been here," he says.

"That may be the case, but they're not the easiest to take on board, or the most comfortable."

"You see the blue sky out there, Tom?"

"Yes."

"Imagine the ideas we talk about are the clear blue sky you see above," he says. "It is always there. Sometimes a cloud might drift across, but behind the blue sky still exists. The more clouds that come, the more the blue sky is covered; but it is still there. The clouds represent the thoughts you have that block the ideas I offer you. The more you have those thoughts, the more clouds there are and the more the blue becomes obscured. The thoughts cloud your vision. If you do nothing to check your thoughts, eventually the blue sky cannot be seen; it looks like it doesn't exist. But, beyond the clouds, it is still there. Sometimes your thoughts might become negative and dark, just like dark clouds on an overcast day. Now, imagine you live in a world where there were only dark clouds above. If you had never seen blue sky, how would you know it existed? But it would still be there, beyond the clouds. Sometimes you may need to clear the thoughts that come up and block that clear view. Sometimes thinking differently helps move the clouds. Become aware of your blocking thoughts and you open the possibility of seeing something else. Then, you might be able to feel the warmth of the sun's rays on your skin."

"Seems it's been cloudy for a while now," I say, still gazing out of the window.

"I know," Gabriel answers with a reassuring voice. "The journey to creating change in your life, or how you are, is not always an easy one. But I am here as your guide; I am here to help you." He places a hand on my shoulder and I feel a warmth radiating through me like a shaft of sunlight breaking through a dark day. I turn to look at him. "We have time; there is no need to rush. We can stop at any moment, you can rest whenever you like and, as I've said, you can ask questions any time." He holds my gaze for a moment. "I should imagine it's like you have been sitting in a room with low lighting and I've just come in and switched on a bright light. All of a sudden you see what the room *really* looks like. If someone were sitting in the room with you, you probably thought you had a good idea of what they looked like, but when the light comes on you finally see them for who they truly are. Perhaps you are seeing yourself for who you truly are, and maybe you don't like what you see. However, the light has been switched on, Tom, and once it's on, it stays on. You are going to see things more clearly now, with different eyes."

"Thanks," I say, with a sarcastic tone, letting him know I'm not actually that grateful for what he's offered.

"There is a difference between living life passively and taking more responsibility. Stepping out of the dark and moving beyond takes courage. It's much easier to blame others, to point the finger at other people, to say *they* made you do something; or to blame situations and events that have happened. But what level of responsibility are you taking with that outlook?"

"I don't have that outlook. What you describe sounds more like the perspective of a victim and I'm certainly not that!" I say. As much as I am hearing what he is saying and starting to understand, I still find myself resisting him and his ideas. It feels like I have something to defend, though I'm not really sure what.

"Of course you are not a victim. You are the *result* of your life to date, rather than a victim of your life to date. I have merely taken the blinkers away, I have been honest and truthful with you, and you are absorbing the reality that comes with that. Many lives are lived without the knowledge that honesty and truth bring; many lives are lived without knowing what you now know. You are learning to accommodate the reality I bring. Please bear in mind that this is probably the most uncomfortable part of what I have to offer. Once you accept what I offer, you will be in a much better position to move forward, in whatever way you choose."

In the silence that follows I move over to sit back down. "I think it is time for you to rest now," Gabriel says, as I slump into the welcoming comfort of the sofa. And with that the room begins to fade, with all the colour paling into nothingness. My eyes become heavy and I drift off with a sensation of being wrapped in a soft, warm blanket, my head drooping as I fall into a state of welcome oblivion.

Turning point

A warm breeze blows softly across my face and stirs me from my slumber. It takes a couple of seconds for me to adjust to a turquoise sky with fluffy cotton wool clouds sparsely scattered across it. In the distance I hear the distinctive sound of children in a school playground, laughing loudly, screaming at each other and running excitedly around. The carefree abandon of childhood enthusiasm at merely being alive wafts through the air, flickering with intensity as the wind carries it, teasing my ears as I lie looking up at the sky absorbed by the clouds drifting by. Closing my eyes, I take a deep breath into my belly, smelling the purity of fresh air and nature around me and enjoying the warmth of the sun on my face. Above the sound of children playing, I hear the faint song of sky larks as they circle and swoop up high. I feel the earth beneath as it holds me, allowing my body to relax onto it. My arms stretch outwards, my fingers running through the mixture of smooth and course blades of thick grass. I listen to life all around me, inhale the freshness of nature and feel the strength of the earth beneath me.

A voice breaks into the peace flaring my eyes open, "Another beautiful day in paradise!" I sharply turn my head in the direction of Gabriel's familiar but disturbing voice. He is sitting on the grass to my right, looking ahead with his arms wrapped around his knees up by his chest. "Life is so simple for children; so pure. But it doesn't take long before things become complicated. The essence of purity lies within the grasp of all children; it's such a shame it becomes lost as they grow up. Yet you are all children at one point, you all have that purity and sense of freedom," he says, with a barely audible sigh. "I like to come here every now and then, just to watch people."

"Can people see you?" I enquire, lifting myself up to rest on an elbow.

"No. Not when I'm here just to observe."

"Observe?" I'm curious what he means by that.

"Oh, people," he says, still looking straight ahead. "Events." He turns his head towards me. "Life."

"How often do you do that then?"

"Oh, I like to come when I have some spare time; if I am not guiding someone," he says, turning to face forward again.

"Like me?"

"Yes, Tom; like you," he says, with a smile.

"Can people see me?"

"No, you can't be seen; you can't be in two places at once," he says, turning to look at me. "In this world you are in a hospital bed, in a coma. Imagine if someone who knows you were to recognise you here, it would be confusing for them and could lead to complications. No, you are here with me and you can sense everything as if you were here in the flesh, but if someone were to pass by, right now, they wouldn't see or hear either of us."

"So, are you never seen or heard in the real world then?" I ask, keen to understand more about him.

"Oh I am!" he replies. "People see and hear me when I want them to, when it benefits them."

What an unusual thing to say. Yet, again, he's managed to make it sound like an everyday event. I have to know more. "When would that be then?"

"Well, you can see and hear me now. We are together in this world right now; are we not?"

"Yees," I say, elongating the word to express my uncertainty. Given the context of the conversation I'm not sure if this *is* a dream playing out or whether we are actually in the real world right now. His logic isn't adding up for me. "But we can't be seen?" I say, my confused tone questioning in response.

"Yes; because it wouldn't benefit them to see or hear us. But it benefits *you* to see and hear me while being here."

"Do you have any idea how confusing you can be sometimes, Gabriel? I can see and hear you in this world, but others can't," I pause, pulling myself up to a sitting position, "but there are times when people in this world *can* see and hear you. Have I got that right?"

"Yes. Sometimes they see me, sometimes they hear me and sometimes they see and hear me."

"How?"

"It's good that you are inquisitive, but I can't explain everything to you," he says with a shake of his head.

"Oh come on Gabriel! You can't say things like that and not expect questions to be asked?" I leap in before he can say any more.

"Do not try to assess being with me by the standards you have come to know and understand in your world," he says, lifting his head to look back at me. "There are other possibilities beyond what you know and understand, and they will not all necessarily become apparent to this world. Time reveals what it is capable of revealing. This world does not need to know everything, Tom. But, yes, I can be seen and heard here, if I want to be. I can bring you here to see, hear, smell, feel and even taste this world; all these things are possible in the realm beyond that which you have become accustomed to," his soft blue eyes delve into me; then he turns to look down the hill. "It's a beautiful day," he carries on, as if the previous conversation hadn't taken place at all. "I hope you slept well."

"Er… Yeah!" I reply, somewhat baffled by the conversation and its sudden shift. "I think I did," I lift my voice to match Gabriel's lighter tone.

"Good. And how are you feeling?"

I pause to consider my response. "Well, with the exception of being a little confused by what you just said, I'm fine. Perhaps a little bruised by the conversation about awareness and acceptance though," I say. Turning to look ahead of me for the first time I see that we are atop a hill overlooking a town which stretches out below us. At the foot of the hill is the school where the children are playing; not actually as far away as the noise of their play had led me to believe. Children run around the play ground; some play football, frantically chasing the ball; some play with a skipping rope, taking it in turns to run in and jump in rhythm with the twists of the rope; some gather in small groups chatting and laughing; some meander from group to group and some walk alone not talking or playing with anyone. It looks just like any school play ground in any town or city.

"You're doing very well at coming to terms with the ideas, Tom. I know they can be uncomfortable, but then not all of life's wonders are immediate and easy to perceive. In fact, seeing beyond the easy and immediate allows you to discover the truly amazing, to see just what you may be able to achieve with your life," he pauses, as if to make sure he has my attention. "Scratch the surface and what you find beneath is often really quite simple. Take something which is deemed to be complicated in its nature, for example, and break it down into its component parts and what do you find?" But before I can answer, he continues. "That it usually is comprised of other smaller, often simple elements."

"Yes, but, not all those elements are simple or easy to explain," I say, unable to entirely agree with his logic.

"Ah, but if you look at it for long enough, you will see that it can be simplified and understood. Once it's understood, you can start to accept it for what it is and what it does. Sometimes, looking beneath the surface allows you to explore and discover what was already there."

This is a rather intriguing and broad statement to make, and I can't help feeling it needs further clarification. "Are you saying that nothing is new then?"

"Oh some things are definitely created a-new, I cannot deny that; however they come from mankind understanding what exists already and applying knowledge to create something anew. In fact, I am constantly amazed at mankind's ability to create new things using what was already there. Do you think Einstein created relativity? Or that Newton created gravity? No, these things and others like them were discovered; they existed beforehand. It is only Newton and Einstein thinking about and understanding them that allowed mankind to harness the idea and use it to create new possibilities. What I am saying is, scratch the surface and you will discover what was always there. By thinking along a certain path you may discover what already existed. Think about it for long enough and you might understand and learn from it. In your case you are thinking about awareness and acceptance, you are learning about them and starting to understand them."

I grimace, wanting to challenge some of what Gabriel has been saying. "I think I understand the idea behind acceptance. I'm just not a hundred percent with it; I struggle to accept certain aspects. For example, it'd be hard to accept something happening to you that isn't of your own doing, but which influences you and how you live your life. Like being struck by a debilitating illness; or being a victim of an earthquake and losing your home. These things would affect you and how you live. Life throws many things at us. I mean, if I were born with only one leg or a condition that meant I'd struggle to live a *normal* life, it'd be difficult to accept how much that'd affect what I could achieve and how I live my life. Not all of these things are created by us and we certainly don't attract them; we can't take responsibility for making them happen and how our lives subsequently pan out, can we?"

"That's a very good point. Let me remind you that this is one of the most uncomfortable areas to take on board; what I am about to say may be even harder.

"It is easier to shift blame onto others, or to say that I am here today not because of what I have done but because of what others have done to me; or because of events, circumstances and situations that have happened around me or to me. You are right, certain things do happen that are beyond your control, such as some illnesses, physical conditions people are born with or acquire; people's gender, race or creed, even height and other physical conditions are beyond control. They are, as you might say, what nature gives you. Unfortunate things happen to people which they don't invite, but which do happen. Things like earthquakes, droughts, floods, tsunamis, hurricanes happen; and if they happen to you or close to you they affect you or what you have. So, I agree, there are things that happen outside a direct sphere of influence or control. The difference, however, is the way people *respond* to the situation. If someone chooses to let something affect them, they are being *at* the affect of it."

I look quizzically back at him; not sure what this odd phrase means. Am I supposed to understand?

"In other words, they *allow* the situation to affect them." He stops for a moment to check how I am taking his words; then carries on. "The alternative is to accept the truth of the situation and do what you can with what you have. The extent to which people accept the reality of what has happened and do what they can with it, makes a difference, Tom." He stops again, allowing me to absorb what he's just said. "If you accept what has happened, or is happening, you free yourself up emotionally and are then able to alter how you respond to the situation. In short, it is how you choose to respond to situations, conditions, events and circumstances that determines who you are and how you experience life."

He looks into my eyes, as if scanning to ensure I have understood him, then down to the children in the school playground; and as he does his face lights up with a smile conveying what can only be described pure love and enjoyment at what he is sees. For him it is easy to jump from deep conversation to sheer pleasure in something completely different and unrelated. Meanwhile, I am still digesting his latest offering. *'It's how you respond to a situation that determines who we are and how you experience life!'* Wow, he delivered that message as if it is common knowledge and everyday speak to him, but it's different for me. He's warned me that it might be hard to take on board, and he wasn't wrong. I've been used to living my life from day to day, and pretty much allowing stuff that happens around me, and *to* me, to affect me. But isn't that the way of the world? OK, so my life isn't perfect, but none of those extreme things had happened to me. I think of myself as one of the lucky ones because I am free of such things. Then I remember that the only reason I'm talking with Gabriel is because I have been involved in an accident that's left me in a coma. I have actually experienced one of those things. Perhaps Gabriel is telling me to take care how I respond to the situation I find myself in. If I am to go back to my life, is it possible that I might be disabled in some way? Certainly it's possible that my life might not be physically, mentally or emotionally as it had been before the crash. Am I being forewarned? "Are you telling me that I might be affected by the accident when I go back to my life Gabriel?"

He turns to face me. "No, that is not what I am saying. Remember, we don't know whether you will return. I cannot foretell the future."

More silence hangs between us.

He continues. "But many people are affected by events and situations they experience and, yes, some people's lives are affected by injury or illness. The difference is how they respond to what life presents them. If you were to go back to your life, and let us say you were paralysed, what would you do? How would you respond to that? Would you allow yourself to be at the affect of that situation, or would you choose to accept it and move forward with what life had presented you with?"

That is a pretty heavy idea to respond to. I take a moment to think before deciding that the best answer is the truth. "I don't know. It's very difficult to answer such a question. Even though it *could* be something I have to face up to soon, it's not what I'm actually facing right now, in *this* moment. What feels real is that I am here with you and I appear fine. But, to answer your question, if I were actually in that situation it would certainly focus my thoughts. For now though, I'd just be happy at being given the chance to be alive, to go back and live."

"So, are you telling me that you'd be happy to be alive, even if you were paralysed? Because *that* is the question I'm asking. How would you respond to *that* situation? Could you make the best of being alive?"

"This isn't an easy conversation to have, Gabriel," I admit. "I guess I'd have to. I'm sure I'd go through anger and fear about being paralysed and having lost my life as I'd previously known it; but eventually I'd have to accept my situation and get on with life."

"What you have just described is the ultimate form of acceptance: accepting what life presents you with, regardless of how extreme it may be, and choosing to respond positively to it."

This is a step too far for me. "Oh, come on, Gabriel, you can't be happy about everything that happens to you."

"I never mentioned happiness. Where did you get that idea from?" he asks.

"You just said it."

"No. I talked about responding positively."

"Doesn't that mean the same? Be happy about it?"

"No, it doesn't; it means accepting what comes and responding from a positive mindset; meaning you *choose* to do something about it or with it, rather than be at the affect of it."

"Right," I say hesitantly, not sure I've completely understood the distinction.

He carries on. "Sometimes it's about accepting an actual physical experience, like being paralysed; or it could be about accepting and coming to terms with a piece of knowledge you don't like. Either way, that is acceptance," he says, offering me one of his smiles, before turning to look down the hill. "You see that girl down there in the playground? Playing football with the other boys and girls. The one with short blonde hair; she's standing still at the moment, catching her breath?"

"Where?" I say, searching the playground. "Oh, the one in the blue top? Is that the one you're talking about?"

"That's the one; she's just started running again. She doesn't seem that fast, but Sophie there won a gold sprint medal at the Olympics."

"What do you mean, *won* a medal? You're talking in the past tense, yet she's only, what, ten years old? She can't win a medal at the Olympics for years to come, she's far too young."

"Of course she's too young, at the moment. But would you like to see her win the medal though?" he asks, with an air of impish excitement.

"What? Are you serious? We don't half have some strange conversations," I say, in disbelief. "First you bring me to a place where people can't see me, yet I can sense *everything* as if I were here in the flesh. You say you come here whenever you want and sometimes people see and hear you, but only when *you* want them to. And *now* you're asking if I want to see someone win a gold medal at the Olympics, when here she is playing as a child in front of me. What are you saying now? Are you telling me you can move around in time?" I ask, wondering just where he's going this time.

He just smiles his usual disarming smile as he turns to face me, his eyes beaming with a cheeky twinkle. "Yes, Tom, I can. But only moments that have already happened. I cannot take you to the future; some things are just not possible," he says, widening his eyes with a 'C'mon now, don't be ridiculous' look.

I look at him bemused by what he expresses with such apparent logic.

"As I said before, do not try to compare the world I show you with the world you have come to know. There are other possibilities out there. Remember when we first met? All the images that came to you? They were from your past. So it is I can show you what has been, but I cannot show you what will be, because the future has not yet happened.

"Look at photographs; they are images of things that have happened in your life. And memories are recollections of things, people and emotions you have encountered already."

"But, I can imagine things that haven't yet happened, can't I? I can picture how something might be," I say.

"Ah, that is a visualisation, an illusion you are creating. Sure, if you visualise hard enough and project how you want your future to be, you increase the likelihood of it being that way. But there are no certainties about the future, we've already established that. What you visualise hasn't actually happened yet, so it is impossible for me to take you to it. But I *can* take you to a moment in time that has happened, a moment that isn't a projection of what *might* happen," he says, raising his eyebrows again, as if he's reached a logical conclusion.

Whilst he blows me away with the idea, there is enough logic in what he just said for me to grasp hold of. But, as usual, he raises another question. "So you can take me to see other people's memories? Not just mine?"

"Yes," he says with a simplicity reserved for those accustomed to what others find unusual. "It's time for you to accept that in my world certain things are possible that aren't in yours. You've seen how I can show you moments from your life; you've experienced them exactly as they were when they occurred in your life. If that can happen, how would I not be able to show you other past moments in time? If it has already happened, then it is out there in time," he says, tilting his head and lifting his eyebrows and raising his hands, palms outwards. "And if it is out there in time, I can take you there. So, yes, I can show you other people's moments in time; I can show you other people's memories. But only if it suits our purpose, Tom. I wouldn't be appropriate to show you someone's past just because you want to have a look. What I show you has to be in line with what *you* are exploring. There have to be guidelines, otherwise we end up with chaos and that doesn't do any of us any good," he says with a tone indicating that he speaks from experience.

I decide to give in and accept what he's saying, even though the logic is alien to me. "OK. I understand. Or, at least, I *accept* what you're telling me." As I speak the blue sky around Gabriel's head begins to drain away as if someone has unplugged the colour. All around and beneath me the grass is fading lighter and lighter; the school playground now looks like a ghost image of what had been there and the town in the distance has already disappeared to whiteness. This is just like when I first awoke in the white space, with images from my life fading away. But having the grass beneath me disappear is a very disconcerting experience. The world I'm in is actually disappearing from all around me, fading to white, and as it does so a sense of anxiety builds inside. I want to hold on to something to help me feel more secure, but there is nothing. All of a sudden I am suspended in a white space again, with nothing to support or hold me up. The feeling of imbalance magnifies, my brain trying desperately to find something to latch on to, to help me feel more stable.

Gabriel notices my discomfort. "Are you alright?"

"Not really," I say, feeling a little sick with the imbalance; throwing my arms out in an attempt to regain lost stability.

"You will get used to this. It's only because your senses are not familiar with it yet that you feel as strange as you do. Don't worry, you won't fall."

"Easy for you to say!" I look around, sat on a non-existent floor. "This is very unnerving." It's as if the field, school and town had never existed; all around is white again.

"Only because you are not used to it. It doesn't last long. In fact, look, here comes the moment we're looking for," he says, making it sound like a bus is coming.

Sure enough, as the image of the hill and school playground had disappeared, so a new image is appearing around us. A general colour bleeds into the whiteness, forming a shape, becoming darker and more cleanly defined. Around us a stadium is materialising and as it tunes into clear vision a buzzing noise gets louder and louder, until I recognise it as the hubbub of thousands of people. Beneath where we are sitting, green grass returns, becoming darker and darker until it is as real as grass I can touch and feel. Again my fingers move through the blades and am reassured by the texture and the feel of solid earth. I look around to get a better idea of where we are and see that we're sitting on the grass in an athletics stadium, close to the edge of the track. Raised above the crowds of people I see the Olympic torch burning brilliantly. Gabriel rises to his feet as I take in the space and activities around me. People are milling all around us on the grass and, close to the track, there are people with clip boards, tape measures, walkie-talkies and clothes that mark them out as officials. More striking than anything else, though, are the athletes dressed in their national colours; they are different to what I was expecting, because every one of them is disabled in some way.

I stand and walk over to join Gabriel. "These are the Paralympics!" I say confidently, as if I've just discovered something interesting and need to let others in on the news.

"Yes, they are," he says, looking around the place with a proud smile. "And this is where we see acceptance at its finest. Look, there is Sophie." He points over to the top end of the track where athletes are limbering up, stretching their muscles and practising their starts. "There, third lane from the left, do you see her?"

There are several people looking like athletes ahead on the track, but surely too many for a sprint race and they are all tethered at the wrist in pairs. "Which one is she?" I ask. "There are two in each lane and they're attached to each other. What's going on?"

"Sophie is blind, she's the blonde lady with long white socks and sunglasses, she's attached to a dark haired woman; she's her guide. That is how blind athletes run, they have a guide to help steer them in the race."

"Oh I see. But she wasn't blind when I saw her before. What happened?"

"No she wasn't blind, you're right; she went blind at age 19, when glaucoma took her sight. That was three years ago now, which has been a challenging journey for her. As you pointed out, Tom, you would probably go through anger and fear if you found out you were paralysed, what would you go through if you lost your eyesight?"

"Well, I think I'd probably go through the same emotions."

"Yes. And many other emotions come when you are confronted with situations like these. Sophie certainly went through anger and fear, she also went through denial and depression; but eventually she realised the truth of the matter; that she was blind and she had to come to terms with it. She chose to accept the reality of what life had presented her and to make the best of what she had. The same is true of all the other athletes in this race, all the athletes at these Paralympics, they have all accepted what life has dealt them and decided to do what they can with what they have. Now," he says with hints of glee and anticipation, "watch the race; it's about to start."

Gabriel hasn't taken his eyes off Sophie while he's been talking to me. As he stops speaking I turn to look at the athletes, all crouched at the top of the 100 metre track, their heads and shoulders bowed down. The noise of the stadium dips to a murmur just above silence as the athletes wait for the gun to signal the start of the race. The official speaks, "On your marks." Silence eases into the stadium. "Set." The gap seems too long. *Crack*, the gunshot pierces the air as the athletes lift to start the race, their heads still down, legs and arms pumping as they race down the track. The crowd roar back in to life, cheering the runners on. Each guide tethered to the sprinter stays just behind them as they run, shouting directions and telling them where the other athletes are in comparison. Within seconds the athletes whizz past us, Sophie pulling ahead, crossing the finish line first. She keeps on running beyond the line, as her guide helps her slow down to a stop; and then she bends over, places her hands on her thighs, gasping for breath. Her guide hugs her in celebration. Then she straightens up and begins jumping around excitedly. I can't hear her above the noise of the crowd in the stadium, but I can see her screaming in ecstasy, her face expressing complete joy. Although Sophie can't see it, the clock by the finish line shows an impressive 11.36 seconds. She has won the gold at the Paralympics just as Gabriel said, and only three years after going blind.

Elations wells up inside me as I am sucked into the excitement of Sophie's victory and the electric atmosphere around us; "Wow! That's incredible!" I turn to talk to Gabriel and am immediately taken back by what I see; his face is alive, expressing sheer delight at being here enjoying this spectacle. I never thought it possible to see him like this; his normally calm demeanour gone, replaced by what can only be described as the very human emotion of exhilaration. He is plainly proud of Sophie. As I watch him in awe, I see that while he had initially been looking at Sophie, he is now taking in all the athletes from the race with the same expression of admiration.

"You seem proud, Gabriel," I bellow, to make sure he hears me.

"Yes, I *am* proud," he says, turning to me. "I am proud because all these people are living proof of what you can achieve when you accept what life brings you. When you choose to do what you can with what you have. Do you understand the idea of acceptance now? Do you see that it doesn't matter whether you created something happening in your life or if it was an external factor that affected you, so long as you accept the reality of the situation?" he is positively radiant with energy as he speaks.

"Yes, I do," I say, as I join him in looking admiringly at the athletes in the stadium.

"Good." He comes closer to make sure I hear him through all the noise in the stadium. I tear my eyes from the runners to focus my attention on him. "I brought you here to see this, so you could understand the ultimate in acceptance. But acceptance does not have to be as magnificent as this, it is not just about how you deal with or respond to the difficult situations you encounter or what you have in your life. This," he opens his arms out as if to encompass the whole stadium, "is to highlight what can happen if you accept situations that are beyond your control. The essence behind acceptance is quite simple though – accept that you create your own realities by the decisions you make, by what you do, what you say and how you respond to what life offers you. You generate the experience of your life by how you interact with it. If you want something about your life to be different you must accept this before making any decision to change it. Acceptance is the art of freeing yourself from what has been or is." He pulls away briefly and offers one of his embracing smiles, then coming closer again, he continues, "Be open to the possibility of things being different, accept the part you play in creating your life being as it is and, perhaps, if you admit to being imperfect, maybe, just maybe, you will free yourself from self-imposed constraints. Maybe your life and how you experience it *could* be different," he stops speaking but continues to gaze into my eyes and keep my attention as if he is still speaking. "Nothing can be different unless you grasp the importance of awareness and acceptance, Tom." With this he lifts his arms to place his hands on my shoulders and draws me closer "How are you doing?" he asks reassuringly.

"I'm doing OK, I think. It's all a bit new to me, you know? It's certainly not easy to accept it all," I say, "I think I'm getting there. But I wasn't aware I needed to change anything in my life, before you came along."

"Don't worry yourself too much about that right now; I am not saying you *need* to change anything. However, if you *want* to, then that is a different thing altogether. Do not rush to make any rash decisions; you need some time to assess where you are with your life right now. I think you need to let all this settle in a bit."

"Oh, you're right," I say, recognising the magnitude of just how much there is to take in. "I've a lot to mull over. Maybe I... Well, let's just put it this way, maybe there are certain things about my life that need reconsidering."

Gabriel nods as he looks at me, his hands still resting on my shoulders. "If you allow your mind to carry on as it has until now you will only create more of the same in your life. In order to create change you need to accept that, to a greater or lesser extent, how you respond to what you experience in your life influences how you perceive your life. But, Tom, can I ask you to do me a favour?"

This is a turn in proceedings, Gabriel asking me for a favour. I'm curious, "What sort of favour are you talking about?"

"Don't be too hard on yourself." I hear his words, but it's his eyes that touch me most. They signal a level of care I haven't encountered since childhood. "Forgiveness is an important aspect of acceptance. Do not blame yourself for the part you played in creating your life being how it is. Moreover, learn from it. Until this point you haven't had this level of awareness. If you recognise something you may have done that you now see as not being helpful, then accept it, learn from it and move on. I have never met anyone who is perfect; in fact, perfection is not a good model to follow, and being hard on yourself never helps. The art lies in identifying events, in recognising and understanding your responses without judging yourself harshly; in forgiving yourself, learning and choosing to move forward. You are fallible, Tom; you are human after all. Life is not about perfection, it's about the journey; learn where you can and keep giving yourself a chance to try things differently. Until the moment you die it is possible to change how you approach and live your life."

"But I might die, Gabriel!" I blurt out, almost in desperation. "Right now I might *not* get a chance to go back and try a different way."

"Yes, that is true. But, remember, until something has happened it is not a certainty, is it?" he calmly offers.

"Why can't you tell me if I'm going to live? What's the point of having these conversations if I'm going to die anyway?" I am no longer speaking out of anger, this is desperation welling up. Having come this far with Gabriel I want to be given the chance to go back and live, to put the lessons I'm gradually learning into practice.

"Better to have the conversation than not have the conversation. How many conversations have gone unsaid in your life that you wish you'd had?

"Yeah, well... I think we all suffer from that one. There certainly have been conversations I could, or *should*, have had," I admit, "But who hasn't? We all have things we wish we'd said, but didn't."

"A world could be filled with the things that have gone unsaid. Too many people regret not having made the time to say things to others that could have resolved situations or allowed a different perspective. But being willing to have the conversation with yourself is every bit as important as speaking to someone else. At least you are having this conversation with yourself now, Tom. It's a chance to be honest with yourself. Sometimes it is important to acknowledge things to yourself before acknowledging them to others, if indeed you need to acknowledge them to anyone else. The best truth comes when it is told to yourself. To not have this conversation would be like walking blindly among the beauty and wonder of what is possible. You have the ability to adapt and change your behaviour, because you are able to think, to comprehend and understand. All of that comes because you are able to have *this* conversation, with me, and with yourself."

"So, talking to yourself isn't such a bad thing then, eh?" I cheekily retort. "It's not a sign of insanity after all?"

He laughs gently. "No, it is not a sign of insanity; but doing the same things over and over while expecting different results might be!"

"What do you mean?"

"I think it's time for you to rest again. Come, let us leave this magnificent place."

"But that sounds interesting, Gabriel, can't we talk about that?" I ask.

"Next time," he replies, and with that, the stadium dims, its colours draining away. As the image fades, so does my consciousness; my eyes grow heavy and a state of oblivious slumber creeps over me.

Balance

I struggle to make out where I am as sunshine forces a subdued light through closed curtains into a room. "Hello!" comes Gabriel's greeting from my left, announcing I'm not alone.

I turn rapidly to face him, "Oh; hello," the darkness encouraging a hushed tone. "Where are we?" I ask curious to what he's lined up for me this time.

"We're in someone's bedroom. They're about to wake up and I want you to pay attention to what you see and hear."

"OK," I nod a whispered response.

"It is all right, Tom. Remember, you can't be heard."

"Oh, yeah, right, I forgot. It's not easy getting used to that you know!" I say, still barely raising my voice above a whisper. "This does feel a little voyeuristic though, watching someone in their bedroom."

"I know! But I will never take you to an inappropriate place; that would be a misuse of my abilities," he says, and despite not being able to see his face clearly, I pick up a tone of irony. I think he's starting to relax with me. "Every visit we make serves a purpose. You will get used to the idea of not being heard or seen, eventually!"

"So, whose room is it then?" I enquire, looking around; my eyes acclimatising to the soft light. We are standing in the corner of the room. In the opposite corner is a double bed with the shape of a sleeping body formed beneath the duvet, snuggled up against a wall. In the same corner about a foot above the bed is a crescent shelf supporting a lone photo frame. On the other side of the bed, by the doorway, is a bed side table and on it a lamp, a book and an alarm clock, its display piercing the dark with a red 06:48. To our right is a wardrobe and to the left are the thin curtains, seeping morning sunlight in to the room. Beyond them, a set of drawers adorned with personal toiletries, keys and loose change.

"Don't get too wrapped up in whose room this is, pay more attention to what happens here," he says.

"OK," I reply, looking at the shape in the bed. "But it feels strange being in someone's bedroom when they're asleep. It's like we're prying."

"Do not worry; we are not prying on anyone. As usual, this is a lesson."

"And the lesson today is..?" I leave my words hanging for Gabriel to finish, hoping he'll catch my attempt at humour.

"More of the same, Tom. Just showing you different perspectives." And as he speaks something enters the room at pace and jumps on the bed. It doesn't take long to work out what the creature is because as soon as it's on the bed, it starts barking loudly. The dog's bark is so loud and intense it fills the room instantly. The shape in the bed shoots bolt upright, brought sharply from a world of dreams. The dog continues barking and starts bouncing on what I now recognise as a young man, struggling to come to terms with how he's been jolted from his slumber. He tries to calm the dog down but in doing so is knocked backwards, his head hitting the crescent shelf above the bed. The shelf has obviously not been properly secured, as it lifts off its supporting brackets and comes crashing down on the man, the picture frame hitting his shoulder and scaring the dog, who backs away, barking excitedly. Instantly, the man gives out a yelp throwing his hands up to cover the back of his head. He groans as if in pain and, I sense, regret; sounding like someone waking with a hangover, before muttering, "Bloody shelf!" He rubs his head to soothe the pain, and the dog continues barking. The man angles his face to look at the dog and in a loud whisper utters, "Shut up!" But the dog just keeps on barking. The man dips his head in despair, then raises his voice to command the dog with, "SHUT UP!" This time the dog obeys; but continues staring at the man, his tongue hanging out of his open mouth. "Off!" The man commands in a voice that denotes he is now fully awake, and he waves a distinct signal to the dog. The dog jumps off the bed, but then completely catches me out by coming straight over to where Gabriel and I are standing. Not being a big fan of dogs, and this is a large one, I back off instinctively. But my movement attracts its attention and it tilts its head, looking straight at me in fascination.

"I thought you said we couldn't be seen," I whisper out of the side of my mouth to Gabriel, trying not to move. Surely he's got it wrong this time; the dog can see me. If I'm still and quiet, maybe it will ignore me and go away.

"Don't worry, we can't be seen, or heard," he replies, speaking instead of whispering. "Dogs do have this knack of sensing when we are near them, but don't worry, it's just a sense; he's being curious, nothing more."

"So, we're OK then?" I say, somewhat relieved, but still doubtful as this dog really does seem to be looking straight at me.

"Perfectly! The dog might bark, but he won't do anything more because he can't actually see or hear us. Relax Tom; you'll be fine. He'll give up being curious soon enough."

While we've been talking, the man has balanced the shelf back on its brackets and placed the picture frame on top. He throws the duvet aside, clambers to the edge of the bed and dangles his legs over, still rubbing his head. Taking a deep intake of breath he launches himself to a standing position, his pyjama bottoms, which had ridden up during the night, unfurl to cover his legs. The dog turns away from us and trots out of the room, stopping by the doorway to take another look over his shoulder in our direction, before then disappearing out of the door, its tail lolloping behind.

"That was strange," I say as the man walks past us, following the dog out of the door and grabbing a towel from a radiator as he leaves the room.

"Yes, and yet it happens every day," Gabriel says, with a matter of fact voice. "The dog rushes in, bounces on the bed and barks Jason awake like that, every morning."

"What's with the shelf though?" I query. "It's too low and surely he needs to secure it? That's very unsafe!"

"Yes. Welcome to Jason's world. He didn't secure the shelf because he wanted to paint it first, but has never got round to painting it, let alone securing it. And he keeps promising himself he is going to do something to stop the dog from waking him that way. Yet, every morning the dog comes in, jumps on the bed and barks loudly to wake him. You would be surprised just how many times he's knocked that shelf; it's always falling off and hitting him somewhere."

"But that's ridiculous; all he has to do is bang in a few nails or put a screw or two in! Can't I do something to help? Surely there's a way for me to..." I hesitate, searching for words. "Surely we can do something to change this ridiculous situation?"

"You are only an observer; you are not allowed to do anything to change or influence anyone other than yourself," he says.

"What about you then? Can't you do something to help here? You've already said that people can hear and see you when you want them to. You seem able to magic things up when you want. Come on, use your powers to help this guy out; it's not like it's a big thing you'll be doing. It would take you no time at all, you could even do it without him knowing," I say, frustrated by the pettiness of the problem.

"You are right, Tom, I could step in, but to do so over small things would lessen the impact and value of what I have to offer. I step in infrequently because, when I do, there is a distinct and specifically beneficial experience to be gained for someone. I must exercise caution in who I speak to and how I act. Mine is not to interfere, but to help where I am needed and where the opportunity is appropriate. There are boundaries; boundaries that are there for a reason and need to be respected. To overstep them could lead to confusion and corrupt the purity of your world. You are one of the few who get to see and experience this with me."

"OK, fine. But *that* is stupid!" I say, pointing over to the shelf. "He's blatantly hurting himself when he could do something, quite simple, to stop it." I'm confused as to why I'm being shown this apparently random scene.

"That is partly why I want you to see this. Things like this happen all over the world, all of the time. I'm showing you this because I want you to see a different version of what I was referring to when last we spoke. Some people hope that things will change, yet they do very little to make them change. They keep doing the same things again and again while expecting different results!"

"That's it! That's what you said just before we left the stadium. You mentioned something about…" I hesitate, pulling at my thoughts to draw back the words. "That's it, you said something, which I think I've heard before actually, something about 'doing the same thing again and again while expecting different results' being insane."

"Ah, so you've heard it before! Good, because those wise words were popularised by Albert Einstein," he says as he moves away from the corner of the room, heading for the door.

"That makes sense," I mutter as I follow.

"Yes. He described doing the same thing over and over again while expecting a different result as insanity. And people tend to pay attention to what Einstein said, don't they?"

"Well, yes, I guess they do." By this time we have reached the head of the stairs, where I make out the sound of what must be Jason's shower running in another room. We start down staircase.

"And yet," Gabriel continues, "while most people will acknowledge him as an intellectual with scientific ideas worthy of attention, it is surprising how some of his other ideas are ignored. They keep doing the same things again and again, in the vain hope that something will turn out differently. That, somehow, *life* will conspire to make the changes for them."

"Yes, but people are like that, Gabriel; they often say one thing and do another. It's, well, it's human nature."

"I know. I've seen that played out time and time again," he says as we walk through a dining room into a kitchen. The dog, by now lying in a dog bed by the side of a radiator, looks up sensing our presence, then rests his head on his front paws, his moist nose just beyond the edge of the bed. Gabriel walks over to a small, wooden circular kitchen table and sits down at one of the chairs. "I hear people saying one thing and doing another all the time. I see people doing the same things over and over again, even when those things seem to be to their detriment; yet they keep doing them. And the thing is, Tom, that the constant repetition of these behaviours and patterns only serves to reinforce them having what they have in their lives. Many people say they want to create change, yet they seem unable to recognise the part they are playing in reinforcing what they already have. You are not unlike Jason you realise? Metaphorically speaking, you keep banging your head on a shelf. You tend to do the same things again and again, which reinforces you having what you have and your life being how it is."

"Oh, come on, Gabriel; I'm nowhere near as obvious as that," I say, gesturing upwards to where we have just come from as I join him at the table.

"No, perhaps not as obvious, I'll give you that."

"So, why are you showing me this?"

"Because I want you to see someone with repetitive patterns which are not doing them any good. I want you to witness someone doing things which, blatantly, are not helping them or their situation."

"Why?" I ask, not sure how this will make a difference to me.

"Because there are those who learn better by witnessing others. When you observe a person or a situation from the outside, it makes it easier to identify repetitive behavioural patterns; and *that* may help you to recognise your own, or at least make things clearer. So, observing Jason might help you see the reality of your situation. Again, it's about looking at things from a different perspective."

"I guess it's like not being able to see the wood for the trees," I say, relating it to what makes sense for me. "So are there things I need to see about myself? Are there things I should be doing differently?"

"That is for you to notice and decide on; it is not for me to tell you. You have a chance to assess your life and how you lead it. Not only has your life been put on pause, you have been given the chance to look at it from a different perspective. To look at it from the outside in. Not many people get this chance you know. As a result, if you feel you would like to make some changes, then it's up to you; it's your choice."

Ever alert to the possibility that I might be going back home, I jump at the chance to probe further. "Now that sounds like I'll be given a chance to go back and try things differently!" I look at Gabriel through quizzical, squinting eyes, thinking I might have found the answer I'm looking for, hoping that he *has* slipped up.

"As much as I'd like to let you know either way, I am afraid I do not know whether you are going back," he smiles recognition back at me for my persistence. "For now you may as well make use of your time in a coma. What else are you going to do with the time you have created?"

Realising that I missed the mark, I swallow my hope and gather myself back in to carry on with the previous conversation. "OK, so it's up to me to choose what I might do differently? *If* I go back that is," I add with a hint of resigned sarcasm.

"Yes. But then it always has been your choice, Tom. You do realise that up until now you have chosen to live the way you have?"

he looks at me as if I should have known what his response would be.

"Oh come on, that's a little harsh," I say. "You've agreed that I didn't know about any of this until now."

"True. You have pretty much followed what you thought others expected of you and what you believed was your path. All I am doing is helping you consider the possibility that things could be different."

"I don't know, Gabriel. I think I'm getting the concept, but it is hard to just... *accept* it," I say, realising the irony of my comment.

"Yes," he nods, sending me a knowing look. "It is."

"So, you're saying that pretty much all I've said and done has led to me being here, at this moment in my life," I say, knowing exactly what answer I'm going to get this time.

"Yes."

"And, according to what you say, even how I've responded to external influences has contributed to this *version* of me?

"Yes."

"But... That's how most people live their lives," I say, feeling the need to state the obvious.

"Yes they do. But most people don't have the kind of pause time *you've* created; they don't meet me and they don't get to have *this* conversation. You *are* one of the lucky ones." In the silence that follows the idea of being lucky finally starts to settle more easily with me. "Providing the majority are happy with things as they are, that's fine," he continues. "On the other hand, if there is something they are not happy with, an aspect they'd like to be different, then maybe it is time to look at doing things differently. There is, after all, only one life as you know it, Tom. You know, some people wake in the morning with a bang to the head, just like Jason, saying they want things to be different, and yet they do nothing to make it different. They complain about it, saying 'life's like that though', just as you have done, and carry on hoping that somehow, mysteriously, things will change without them taking any action. Jason is an unusual version of this, but imagine you were experiencing pain from something and yet you were not willing enough to do something to stop that pain; Einstein's verdict of insanity sounds reasonable to me," he says, leaning back from the table.

"You're right, of course," I admit, with a slight sigh. "But it's not always easy to make the changes necessary to stop this metaphorical pain."

"Change certainly can be difficult. For some, exploring the idea of change highlights the benefits of maintaining the status quo. If, by asking questions and going in the direction of change, you realise you are happy with things staying as they are, then is there any need for change? Opening up and taking a deeper look at their lives leads some people to realise how safe they feel with what they currently have. They feel protected and comforted by what they know and recognise. Added to which, it is often the case that those around them already accept them as they are, so why risk potential upset? Why change?"

"That's perfectly understandable," I say. "I can see how staying within what you know could be appealing to some people; it's *safe* as you say. Yet, now I've had a chance to review my life from *this* side, from a different perspective, I'm starting to think differently." As I speak Jason comes down the stairs and into the kitchen; his arrival heralded by the dog sitting up in his bed and barking again, the abrasive noise breaking the moment I'm sharing with Gabriel.

Jason slides his slippers lazily along the floor as he passes by, his dishevelled hair lying damp along the neck of a dressing gown, which undoubtedly at one point in its life had been white. The dog stops barking, relaxing down in his bed and Gabriel leans in towards me as if about to share a secret. "That dog barks at Jason like that every morning you know? You'd think he'd do something about it!" he glints that knowing look at me again. "Watch this," he says, signalling towards Jason, who now has hold of the kettle and is shuffling to the sink. He opens the lid, runs some water in, closes the lid and sidles back to place the kettle in its cradle. Tentatively he raises his hand to switch the kettle on. Suddenly, there is a sharp but subtle *crack* as Jason jumps back, raising his hand and flicking his fingers with a contained yelp. He sucks his right index finger before then flicking it again as if to alleviate pain. Once again, the dog starts barking.

Gabriel turns back towards me. "Most mornings he gets a slight electric shock from that kettle. Yet he hasn't changed it. You see, the kettle still works and that allows him to have his morning cup of tea. And the dog?" He looks down at the dog, which is by now quietly looking up at Jason through doleful eyes. "Well, the dog still loves him."

I watch as Jason potters on auto pilot round the kitchen preparing a bowl of cereal and making his mug of tea. The kettle gives no shock as he lifts it to pour the boiling water. Then, bowl of cereal in one hand and mug of tea in the other, he slides past us again.

"He gets by, living day to day," Gabriel says as Jason leaves the kitchen. "He'll go off to work in his car, which breaks down every now and then; and he'll promise himself that he'll get a new job soon, one that will afford him enough to buy a new, more reliable car. And so his cycle goes on. Day to day, with very little changing, until, perhaps, life conspires to present him with an opportunity for it to be different. But until that time, he will keep on doing the same things over and over again."

"Just like lots of people!" I say, still looking in the direction Jason went, even though he has by now disappeared into another room, where I can hear the sound of a television presenter reporting the morning news.

"Yes, like lots of people, Tom. It's surprising how many people say they want certain aspects of their life to change, yet they do little to make such change happen."

I turn back to face Gabriel. "But, as you've already said, we don't *all* get to meet with you do we? We don't all have this conversation and gain *this* level of insight," I say, feeling like I'm defending this *mass* of people; after all, until very recently, I've been one of them.

"Yes; but people have choices in life and the choices they make influence the life they have."

"I suppose so," I concede.

"As much as we have talked about there being benefits to life carrying on how it is, there will also be drawbacks."

"Oh yes, undoubtedly there'll be drawbacks," I agree. "I suppose the question is what's the balance between the benefits and the drawbacks? Do the benefits outweigh the drawbacks or vice versa?" I pause for a moment, looking straight at Gabriel as I consider my words. "If the benefits are perceived as greater than the drawbacks, then there may be no need to change anything. Indeed, why change?"

"You have it in a nutshell," he says, smiling, like a teacher proud of his pupil. "The art lies in being able to recognise the benefits and the drawbacks for you personally, and being honest about their impact on you. Once you have done that, it's all about working out where your truth lies in that balance. Let us look at you for a moment."

"OK," I say, curious as to where he's going with this.

"What are the benefits of your life being as it has been?"

"Ooh. Erm," I think for a while, drawing on my memory from when the moments of my life had visited me in the white space. "Well, I certainly earn decent money. My job's good. I have a beautiful daughter. A nice home. My car's..." I pause. "Actually, I was going to say my car's lovely, but I don't actually know what state my car's in right now. I liked that car," I say indignantly, breaking my list, before re-gathering my thoughts and carrying on.

"I have some good friends. I feel pretty safe and secure," my voice trails as my list begins to dry up. "But, Gabriel it's a little difficult for me to assess this accurately, given where I am right now."

"And what about the drawbacks?" he carries on without the slightest acknowledgement of my last comment.

"Well straight away, I don't know if I'm alive or dead. Which, in case you haven't noticed, I'm not entirely happy about!" my quip meets with no sign of a response, so I carry on with a sigh. "My marriage is over. Or at least that's how it's felt up until recently," I hesitate, struggling with the emotions now coming up. "Actually, if I'm really honest with you, with things as they have been, I've been feeling quite lonely; a little down." My body slumps with another sigh, deflating me even further, my head dipping to one side as I break eye contact with Gabriel. Realising just how sad I have been feeling of late. I carry on. "You know… Life hasn't been as fun as it once was," I say quietly, looking back up at him.

"I know. I'm sorry about that," Gabriel offers, sounding as if he genuinely cares. His eyes seem to connect to the very core of me. "Listening to your brief list of benefits, with the exception of Emily and your friends, I hear a lot of material benefits. Yet when I hear your drawbacks, they are mostly emotional. Just notice how when you talk about the drawbacks it sends you into an emotional state. *That* is where I think your truth lies."

"What do you mean by that?" I ask.

"Well, when listing benefits and drawbacks it's not necessarily the length of a list that makes the biggest difference. What can make the biggest difference is your emotional response to something. You might say what feels right or wrong, good or bad. The sense of where the truth lies for you. When people speak their truth it tends to add so much more weight that it tips the balance. When you listed your drawbacks just now, you were being honest with yourself and I believe you spoke your truth. So much so in fact that, for me, it tipped the balance. When the truth regarding how you feel about something is established and accepted, it tends to become *the* determining factor. Ultimately, *it* tips the balance."

"But I didn't feel good about my list of drawbacks, I felt bad; is that still my truth speaking?" I ask, not sure I've fully grasped this.

"Oh yes. The truth can be either. You might have a sense of something not being right for you, but you go ahead with it anyway and it turns out not to work for you. With hindsight you look back afterwards and say 'I knew I shouldn't have done that'. You see, your truth was speaking to you at the time, but your emotional radar was not tuned in, so you weren't able to hear it clearly and act on it. Listen more and you will hear the truth, it is there and it is often emotion speaking."

Of course he is right; when I detailed the list of drawbacks my energy had really dipped, I felt so much lower emotionally. It makes sense now; I had found my truth, even though in the moment I hadn't recognised, or perhaps, *accepted* it. It took Gabriel pointing it out for me to see it. In deep thought I utter a distracted sound of recognition.

"So, having established where the balance lies for you, if the drawbacks outweigh the benefits, the next question is would you like to change things?" Even though the conversation feels heavy for me, Gabriel's voice is not, in fact his tone is quite up-beat.

I pause again, maintaining his deep gaze before opening my mouth. "I think it's pretty obvious that the drawbacks outweigh the benefits here, don't they? And, yes, I think I'd like it to be different."

"Is it possible it could be different, Tom?"

Silence again… "Yes… It is possible… It *could* be different," even through my hesitancy I'm surprised at my admission.

"Good," he says firmly but calmly. Then, leaning in again, with a heavy whisper he says. "By the way, if you ever arrive at a 'No' when answering that question, it is time to revisit the principle of acceptance. Come on," his eyes widen with a smile, "let us leave here." He reaches over and takes my hand, encouraging me to stand as he rises from his chair. The room begins to fade, its colours drain and images become less clear; whiteness swamps the space around us. In the background I make out the sound of a dog's bark, growing fainter.

Desire

We stand hand in hand in the, by now familiar, white space. For a moment I feel imbalanced, but just as Gabriel promised, that sense is definitely waning. What started out as alien to me is beginning to feel safe, rather like a home; a place I can relax away from the strains of feeling a need to be a version of me I've become accustomed to. It's a place where there is no world to recognise; where there is a sense of being at ease with myself, as opposed to a sense of needing to become or do anything. There is no horizon, nothing to delineate where I am, or to determine what context I'm in. This is a blank canvas on which Gabriel paints an image for me to see and feel. A canvas that allows me to experience without being judged and where I'm nurturing a lack of desire to judge.

Out of the whiteness a new scene emerges, forming second by second, becoming more colourful and three dimensional. Ahead I make out wooden shelves appearing, laden with what look to be jars. As it becomes clear these jars are full of sweets, I realise we are standing in a traditional sweet shop; the kind I remember from my childhood. Between me and the shelves of sweets is a counter with bars of chocolate and candy protected from prying hands by a curved glass screen. Replenishing the supply of sweets behind the counter is a fulsome, grey haired lady shopkeeper wearing a white and light blue checked overall, quietly humming a melody I can't make out. A host of familiar names call to me from beyond the glass screen stirring a series of delightful taste sensations from years gone by. It's been such a long time since I was in a shop like this; it must have been when I was in my mid teens. I let go of Gabriel's hand and look around, taking in the wonder of this magical place. The smell of sugar and candy wafts up my nostrils, filling my head and swelling my stomach.

A child enters, dressed in rather outdated clothes, but very much recognisable as a fashion I might have worn when I was that age, going back some thirty years or so. The young boy strides over to the counter and, in a rather proud voice, asks politely for, "A mixed quarter of cola cubes and pineapple chunks, please!" Wow, a quarter of mixed cola cubes and pineapple chunks, gorgeous! What a memory. I can't remember when I'd last had either of them. "Certainly my lovely," the lady says with a broad smile. She turns round, takes two jars of sweets from the shelves behind her and, lifting the lid off both, pours out equal quantities into the measuring bowl on a set of weighing scales. Adding one final cola cube she finds the required balance point, then whips the bowl off the scales and pours its contents into a small white paper bag. Holding on to the edges, she deftly twists the bag over itself a couple of times to seal it. "That'll be twenty pence please love," she utters, and the boy hands over two silver coins, keeping his hand outstretched waiting for the bag. As soon as it's safely in his hand, he turns sharply, his head down as he walks out of the shop. He opens the bag, takes out a yellow cube and, just before shoving it into his mouth, hollers, "Thank you!" And disappears out of the shop into the sunshine.

"I want some of those please!" I say to Gabriel, mimicking the voice of a polite child.

"Are you sure you want those, you could have anything you like. Strawberry bon bons, lemon drops, or how about mint humbugs? he says, sounding like an eager magician able to summon up anything from the shelves of confectionary.

"No, I was only joking," I say, but then see that Gabriel is quite serious. "Oh, well if you're offering, I'd still like to have the cola cube, pineapple chunk mix please," I say in a somewhat more adult voice.

"Of course; hold your hand out," he says and out of nowhere a white paper bag appears in my hand with its two edges turned over in twists to seal it. I open the bag to reveal a mixture of red and yellow sugar coated cubes. Eagerness gets the better of me and I reach in to take a red cola cube and pop it straight in my mouth. The first flavour to hit me is the coarse sugar coating, followed by the distinctive flavour of the slightly acidic cola cube and my taste buds squirt saliva to help my mouth cope with the sensation.

"See; you couldn't resist it, could you?" Gabriel says with a knowing smile.

"No," I reply, struggling to form the word clearly while accommodating the rather angular sweet.

"*That* is why I brought you here. People seldom resist the temptation of being in a sweet shop. For those who have lost touch with the joys and carefree abandon of life, for some reason it seems to stimulate something deep inside."

I suck on my cola cube, looking straight back at Gabriel, my mouth undulating and lips pursing. While I don't say it, I cheekily think 'you mean it stimulates something in their stomach.'

"Desire is a strong sense," he says. "And when people hit *desire* they tend to do whatever it takes to get what they want."

"Hhmmnn," I signal a noise to show I'm still paying attention.

"Desire tends to be a positive expression. If you hear the word desire it is usually associated with a strong, positive, even happy urge for something. Would you agree?" I nod a response. "I would go so far as to say that *desire* is one of those words which represents itself very well; there are few others that can be used in its place. And when desire is felt, a person tends to do whatever is necessary to get that which they desire."

By now the cube has started to smooth at the edges, making it easier to speak. "Yes. It pretty much means that to me too," I garble back at him. Suddenly realising how rude I have been by not offering him a sweet, I hold the bag out in his direction. "Sorry, did you want one?" I ask, somewhat embarrassed.

"Oh, no thank you, Tom," he smiles back at me and carries on. "It is one thing to say you would like something, but until you achieve a sense of desire around it, the chances are it will just stay out there as a 'would like' rather than a 'must have'. Only when you move into a state of desire around wanting something to be different are you likely to achieve it. To create change in your life takes desire, especially as you are invariably battling against a host of *perceived benefits* to things staying as they are. Not only are you battling against the comfort of what has become safe and familiar to you, even habitual; you may also be battling against other people's perceptions, how they have come to know you, the version they recognise and feel safe knowing."

"Well, yes, how people perceive me does matter sometimes. But, go on, tell me more."

"Remember, your actions have a ripple effect on others; so if you decide to make some changes, this will impact on others too. Even if it's just how you are perceived by them. Every action generates a thought, some sort of response in other people's minds. So, even if your change does not directly affect others, it may lead to them thinking differently about you. For the most part that will be fine, but it is important to be considerate of how others might feel in relation to your changes. You see, they will have become accustomed to recognising you as the person they're familiar with; when you change, how they perceive you changes too."

"But that's OK, isn't it? Surely I want others to see the change?" I query, not sure why this might be an issue.

"Ah well, now that raises a different point. Let's look at that briefly. If you are changing so you can be *seen* differently by other people, the question that comes up for me is, who is the change for? Do you own the need for change, or is it for others benefit?"

"Well... I sup...pose..." My mind whirs. As much as I know a change should be for me, if we're talking about me in relation to Louise, then I would want her to see the change. "Well, yes, ultimately the change would be for my sake. But, I'd want Louise to see the change. It might influence how she feels about me and that'd help me achieve what I want; wouldn't it?" I ask. "Surely there are benefits to others seeing the change?"

"If you want others to perceive you differently that is fine; but ultimately you must only make changes because *you* want them. You must *own* the changes, Tom, not make them because of others," he pauses. "If you own the changes they become more real for you and a part of who you are. Consequently your change will be perceived by others as genuine and that, in itself, is more likely to influence how they respond to you."

"OK," I say. "I understand. Be true to yourself and genuine in your desire for change!"

"Yes. But remember; we were not talking about that initially," he looks at me with raised eyebrows. "The point I was making is that you should take care of other people's feelings around how they relate to you, and be willing to accommodate their responses to you. Not everyone will be happy with the changes you make, especially those close to you. Have care around them. Be prepared for them to challenge you and how you have become. When others don't know how to behave around the new you and the changes you make, how they relate to you changes. Because the people close to you form part of your safety, if they respond differently it can give you a sense of insecurity and you may question whether the change is a good idea."

"I see," I haven't considered this before.

"Yes. Be aware that it is possible for your change to create a sense of discomfort, even dissatisfaction in others, possibly even inferiority. Your taking action to create change can lead to others reflecting on what *they* have and how *they* are. It is therefore possible for the changes you make to have an adverse effect on others. You see, in order to create your change you develop a different mindset; a mindset others may not share. They may not like the change you made or the new version of you. You could end up at odds with them. At the very least, it may take them a while to acclimatise to and accept the new version of you."

This is a new idea to me, taking other people's feelings into consideration in this context. I'd just presumed that if I were making a change for the better then it would surely be of benefit to others. "I'm a little confused here... Surely that contradicts what you just said before, about making sure I shouldn't do things for other people, but for myself! Have I missed something here?"

"No you've not missed anything, Tom; the two messages are actually quite complementary. Let me clarify. It is paramount that you only make changes because you *want* to make them, because *you choose* them. But it is equally important that you have consideration for how your change impacts on others." Once again his eyes maintain their hold on me, checking that I'm hearing him clearly. I stay with him, giving a faint nod of acknowledgement. "Be considerate in how you are with others as they take your changes on board. Your changes may not suit others and they may apply pressure for you to not make them. It is also highly likely that others will take a while to adapt to the new version of you; during this time they may behave differently towards you. This is where you need to be considerate. Allow them to have their response as they acclimatise. Do not force your changes on anyone; moreover find ways to help them accept you and your changes."

"I see," I say as it sinks in. "Make the change because I want to but think about how it affects others."

"That's it," he smiles. "Do you see how desire plays an important part here as well? Desire's not just about becoming clear that you want the change; it's also about ensuring you stay committed to it as the change beds in. How others respond may prove difficult for you and may challenge your determination. It is important that you stay *true* to yourself and your desire for change. If you do not desire the change enough, when you encounter obstacles, and there could be many, you may weaken. Desire forms the backbone of your intention to create change; without desire it is possible that you may give up or succumb to pressure from others as they challenge you during the process of change."

As usual, Gabriel has set me to thinking again. He's right, of course; people do give in to pressure from others, and it takes commitment to overcome those kinds of pressures. Actually, it takes *desire* to stay focused on the benefits of creating what we want despite whatever resistance we may encounter. "I know what you mean. In fact, there've been times when I've thought about wanting something, but that's all it's been, *thinking*, nothing more. I'm even guilty of talking about wanting something, but truth is, it's just talk, I haven't had enough desire to make it happen."

"Talking something over is useful, in fact I'm in favour of it as it helps to get your thoughts clear, but talking about doing something is a lot easier than doing it. What's the saying, actions speak louder than words?"

"Ah, that old adage!" I smile. "They certainly do. I think talking about doing something without action is a bit of a national pastime these days. It's almost become acceptable to talk about something and not do it! But, Gabriel, I have a friend who's quite the opposite."

"Is that so? Tell me more."

"She's quite an inspiration actually. Julie rarely says she's going to do something unless she means to do it. What is amazing about her is that she gets it absolutely clear in her head what she wants; she creates a real vision for it and seems to surrounds that vision with... *desire!*" I say, raising my voice as well as pointing a finger in Gabriel's direction as the penny drops. "Such is her ability with this, that when she talks about what she wants or what she is going to do differently, there is a glow about her; her face lights up, her eyes positively shine. It's easy to believe her when she gets that way. You know when someone gets behind their own belief, because they are passionate about it? That's Julie; she becomes enthusiastic and energised around doing it. She makes it happen," I can feel myself getting enthused as I speak. "You know what else? It's contagious. I usually walk away from her with a smile on my face; I want to create some of that magic for myself."

"I can see that she inspires you," he says, appearing quite taken by what I'm saying. "Your energy is very good at the moment, this is the most excited I've seen you. I'd even say that it's *you* who has the glow in your eyes right now. So, you think her way of being has a certain *magic* to it?"

"Yeah! She creates such a strong sense of desire around something that it becomes attractive; actually *she* becomes attractive. There is such a good energy around her desire to achieve something, that I walk away thinking 'I'd like to have some of that energy please'."

"And what do you do with that feeling?" he asks.

"Well, let me put it this way," I say, apologetically elongating my syllables. "I'm afraid it doesn't last."

"Oh. And why is that?"

"Well…" I start. "I walk away feeling good and wanting some of the magic for myself, but, then something or someone comes along that draws my attention away from that sensation. Other things side track me and I find myself in a different state; before I know it I'm back to how I was feeling before…" I stop mid sentence, as a realisation comes to me. "Oh my God, Gabriel! I've just got it! I slip back into being a version of me that reinforces me having what I already have!" I look away from him, my mind ticking over each thought, holding my breath. Then, breathing in again, my eyes come back up to meet his blue eyes, "Is that acceptance?"

"Not far off. I'd say you've just become *aware* of a reinforcing behaviour. Now if you *accept* that your behaviour reinforces you being who you are, having what you have, then yes that is acceptance," he says with a broad smile.

"So I *allow* myself to carry on having what I have?" I probe, searching for confirmation of where my thoughts have taken me.

"Yes." His reassuring word releasing the penny that's dropped in my mind. "You feel good when you are with your friend, but you allow other factors to influence you afterwards; you *allow* yourself to revert to what you have become accustomed to."

My eyes widen. "Is that really how it's been, Gabriel?"

"After years of responding to situations and people the same way you slip into patterns of behaviour which become almost automatic," he says with a perceptible glow about him, happy his student is making progress. "These are the 'default behaviours' you referred to before. They are so much a part of you that they become your preferred patterns of response; they're instinctive emotional responses that reinforce you having what you have. There is no blame for these things, Tom, they are what they are. You formed them out of habit."

"I think some of those habits are pretty well ingrained in me," I admit.

"That is what habits are. Behaviours so well practised they become part of who you are; patterns you enact sometimes without even thinking." For the first time, we're talking on the same wavelength.

"Ah, so we're not always aware of these things then?" I jump in.

"That's correct. The art of awareness is being able to open your eyes and see things as they are, nothing more. Just now you went through the process of becoming aware, didn't you?" I nod. "Which enabled you to move towards acceptance. The good news is that, because these habits are formed by you, you can form new ones. In the moment you become aware of them, you have a choice - either carry on doing the same, recognising that you are doing it, or decide to do something different. Break the pattern that reinforces you creating more of the same coming back," he offers an inviting smile while making what he says sound as logical as one and one equalling two. I realise that there is no contradiction here, it all blends in neatly. He carries on, "By noticing the moments where you repeat those patterns and behaviours, you have the choice as to whether you want to overlay them with new ones. But the key to this lies in making sure you *desire* the change enough to make it happen. You will encounter barriers, you will meet resistance from others and from yourself, but if you *desire* the change enough it is possible to overcome them."

"So, if I change how I am and how I approach things, I can change the life I experience?"

"Exactly, Tom; that is essentially what I have been saying since we first met," he says, with a warm hint of 'I told you so'. "Changing what you do can lead to a different outcome."

"Outcome? Sorry, can you just explain that to me again?"

"Yes. If you break the pattern of doing the same things again and again then you are more likely to create a change in what you get back, the outcome you create," he looks at me as if this is the most straightforward thing in the world.

"Is it really as easy as that?" I ask.

"Remember, something which may appear complicated is often made up of smaller simpler parts. The idea here is simple: by becoming more aware you allow yourself to alter your approach; and it's that change of approach that makes the biggest difference, *it* creates the possibility of a different outcome.

"Of course, I recognise that putting it into practice isn't always that easy. But, I can assure you that if you recognise your patterns and behaviours and, where necessary, you change them, you improve the likelihood of creating a different outcome. It all stems from awareness, Tom."

At that moment three children, no more than ten years old, noisily come into the shop, milling around the counter, peering at the fine selection of confectionary on display. "Can I help you?" the shopkeeper asks in a tone almost as sweet as the confectionary itself. There is no immediate reply from the two boys and girl, each wearing the same school uniform, as they vie for position, muttering to one another trying to work out which is the best sweet to ask for and debating whether they should choose different ones each to then share afterwards. The lady behind the counter is obviously used to this scene as she stands patiently waiting for the children to make their minds up. After much conferring and bickering, the children arrive at a decision they are all happy with. The eldest looking boy places the order, offers payment, receives the stash of goodies and hands them out to the others as they jostle their way out of the shop, their heads down, focused intently on opening their treats.

"If only things were that simple," I say, watching the last one leave the shop, excitedly shoving a Fruit Pastille in her mouth, before running to catch up with the other two.

"It is a shame the innocence of childhood fades. Sadly the protection of not having to think and care for yourself does not last," Gabriel pulls my attention back. "Patterns, behaviours and responses are being laid down from an early age; it does not take long for these children to create their patterns of behaviour. By the time you get to your age, Tom, they are well established, so letting go of them is not easy. They can be so ingrained, that you actually believe *that* is who you are. So, to truly break these patterns, you need to become more aware of how you think. It is no good just saying you want to do something and trying to behave differently; you must start to alter how you think in relation to yourself and whatever it is you want to achieve."

"Is this still part of desire then, Gabriel?" I ask.

"Oh yes," comes his casual reply. "Influence your thoughts and you influence how you are. By creating a strong sense of desire around something you start to alter how you think in relation to it. Your mind is a powerful tool and yet you hardly use it. You are aware of it, yet you do little to understand and tap into its capacity."

This seems a little unfair and yet it matches his approach

perfectly. Just when we're getting somewhere, he says something to interrupt the flow. "That sounds a bit harsh, Gabriel. What are you saying?"

"I am saying that the mind has more potential than it is currently being used for."

"By me?" I'm not sure if this is an attack on me or not. We've just started to understand each other for the first time and this comment has thrown me.

"Yes," comes his response. "But you are not alone, Tom."

That's a relief, but I'm still not sure where we stand. "What do you mean?"

"I mean that the potential of the human mind has yet to be realised," he says in his usual matter of fact way.

I want to know more, "OK, what are we missing out on?"

"You are not *missing* anything, you have everything you need. Just like gravity and relativity were there before they were discovered and named. In time, the potential of the mind will be discovered and used more effectively. For now though, it is sufficient for me to say that if you *think* differently in relation to something, you are likely to create a change. The state of mind you occupy determines the experience you have. If you picture a vision in your mind of something you would like, create enough desire around it and alter the behaviours which impede you, you increase the likelihood of getting or achieving it. But if you do things differently without having first created a mind-set that *believes* in what you are doing, you are less likely to achieve the outcome you want. Desire *has* to come from within; it is no good paying lip service to the idea. Think about the rewards and sensations that will come as a result of making change and picture them as a true reflection of what you want. This is not just about creating whimsical change; it's about visualising a *desired outcome*."

I'm confused, again. "Hold on a minute, though. Before, you said that to visualise something doesn't mean it will happen. The future is made moment by moment, you said."

"Yes, I did, and that is correct. I also said that visualising helps increase the likelihood of something happening. While there are no certainties about the future, the extent to which you desire an outcome and visualise it does influence the likelihood of it happening. It all takes place in your mind, Tom. You are the only one who can create the sense of desire that comes from having a different mind-set around your beliefs."

"So this is about belief then?"

"Oh belief plays a big part, especially at this stage. Belief is what can lead to *real* change."

With that, the sweetshop begins to fade. The sunshine which has been radiating through the windows is replaced with whiteness, and the smell of sugar and candy wanes until it is just a faint recollection. I pop the packet of sweets in the deep pocket of my trousers, not knowing if I will get a chance to sample their memory inducing flavour again. Soon enough, another image begins to form around us. It takes a while to make out where we are.

Belief

We are standing in a centre aisle and to either side rows of wooden benches face uniformly forward, like a carved army poised on bended knee. Beyond them are light coloured walls and partially stained glass windows, reflecting fragments of colour into the spacious room. I follow the direction of the benches and find myself looking at a raised altar, behind which a large crucifix hangs, imposing itself on the room.

"You've brought me to a church!" I say, turning to Gabriel.

"Yes, and how they've changed over the years," he replies, with a nostalgic air. "But then they are only a place for people to come and express their beliefs. What that place looks like isn't important," he pauses, breathing in the space as he scans the room. "It doesn't matter which religion is practised, throughout history the places where people gather to express their beliefs all have a certain feel about them, an aura. Something special happens in places like these," his head lifts upwards to take in the space above. "I find them such calming places to spend time; almost purifying."

"Hmmm," I agree, as I join in looking above and around me. "There is something about them; even when they're empty. I always feel I have to behave myself, like I'm being watched." We share a moment reflecting the peacefulness of the place. "Do you know? It's a while since I've been in a place like this. The nearest to it must have been my father's funeral."

"You are not alone, Tom. Lots of people only go to church these days for weddings and funerals; sometimes for christenings. But even that happens less and less now. Yes, churches are not as popular as they once were," his voice reflects a note of regret as he adds this last point. "But," he starts afresh, "this is as good a place as any for us to talk about belief," he turns to face me, speaking with a warmer, more embracing tone.

A very large penny drops, catching me out; "What? You mean you want to talk about faith?" Is this what he's been building up to all this time?

"No, that's not what I said. We are here to talk about belief," he says, highlighting an apparent difference between belief and faith.

"But you've brought me to a church. Why have you chosen this venue if we're not talking about faith?"

"Because, for centuries, churches and other places of faith, have been where people come to express their beliefs. A sweet shop was purely representational of a place where someone might express desire and, given that children are often the best at expressing the purest form of desire, that is where I took you. Tell me though, Tom, where else would you conjure up as a possible location if I asked you to choose a place representational of belief?"

He's caught me out again. Perhaps because he's already brought me to a church I struggled to come up with a different location. "Actually, now you mention it, I suppose the Paralympics would be just as good a place."

"Yes, you're right," he says with a smile. "Paralympic athletes certainly have a belief in themselves *and* they are expressing their desire for something too; so we could have stayed at the stadium for all our conversations. But I think it's good for you to have variety and some different experiences. Would you like a different location?" he says, sounding willing to create a new setting in an instant.

"No, I guess this place is as good as any," I say, admitting that the venue isn't that important to me.

"I want to talk about beliefs, because they are powerful. Once you believe something it tends to influence how you approach things; and because a belief is a state of mind it is unquestionable;

it is *your* belief. Of course, what can be questioned is *why* you believe something. I can challenge your belief and I can even ask you to reconsider your commitment to your belief, but I can't dispute the fact that you believe it. Such is the power of belief, it is your independence. The good news though, is that you acquire your beliefs, and as such it is possible to acquire new ones. You *can* change your mind."

"Well that's good to know," I say, somewhat mockingly.

"Belief is powerful, Tom, it can change your approach to life and the situations or people you encounter. You are what you believe."

"Ooh careful there, Gabriel; especially in a place like this!" I say. "Look at what has happened throughout history as a result of some people believing they are right and others wrong. One religion saying their way is right and another religion is wrong. Wars have taken place over such things. Even now, people are fighting for religious causes they believe in; people are capable of killing each other because of their beliefs."

"Yes, you are right and that saddens me. I am amazed at what mankind is capable of when it comes to hurting its own," his head dips slightly, "and yes, you are correct, these actions come as a result of people's beliefs. Hurting others in the name of a belief is wrong and always will be; such behaviours cannot be condoned." He sits down on a pew to his side, visibly deflated. I join him, sliding into the pew in front and turn to face him, my arm resting on its back. "But, let me be clear here, these actions taken by man against man are not due to religion; they take place because of a blinkered belief that their way is the *only* way." There is a depth of emotion to how he now speaks, a depth I haven't heard him express before. "The world is a mix of different cultures, religions, ideals and ways of living. Many of these are born out of beliefs that have built up over time; often ideas and ways of being passed from generation to generation and nurtured until they become a belief. It is possible, though, for people to live together even when they have different beliefs; the art lies in understanding other people's beliefs or ideals and being willing to listen to and accommodate them. Divisions often exist because one group tries to force another to take on their belief without considering that there may be a different way. When one culture meets another culture, when one set of beliefs meets another set of beliefs, therein lies the potential for conflict. Unfortunately, this is part of mankind's nature. It is also one of mankind's greatest challenges: to be able to listen to and accommodate others beliefs, to be able to live together." He holds me transfixed as he speaks. This part of our conversation has come out of nowhere, or so it seems; and as I return Gabriel's gaze I see sadness in the blue waters of his eyes. "But, Tom," he resumes, "all of this shows what is possible when the mind believes it is right about something. You talked of war, well, for a moment, let's look at the idea of war from a different perspective. Think about conscientious objectors, people who strongly believe that war and killing others is wrong, be that on religious or ethical grounds. They stand up and say 'I believe *this* is wrong and we should do something to change it'. If enough people stand up and express their belief, therein lies the possibility of change. But it often starts with just one person standing up to express their belief."

I let his words rest as I consider them and my response. "You certainly seem to have a good understanding of people, Gabriel," I say, just as saddened now by the conversation.

"Yes, I do," he replies, with an expression conjuring up a depth of knowledge greater than words alone can convey.

Inspired by what he has said, I carry on, "Do you think Bob Geldof is an example of someone who stood up to be heard?" I pause to check he is familiar with who I'm talking about. He gestures a slight nod to let me know he is with me and encouraging me to carry on. "He expressed an opinion about helping those starving people. He suggested that we should do something to solve the problem rather than just watch it on telly. OK, so he was rather ardent in how he expressed himself, but it was his belief and passion that made something happen. It was his desire to create action, backed by his belief that it could happen, that inspired others to action."

"I'd say so. If a person creates enough desire around something, they become passionate about it and belief follows. That is the case with leaders throughout time; they create a desire around something to the extent that they become passionate about it. They believe what they're saying is right, that others should listen and take action based on what they're saying. Leaders use their own belief to stimulate others into believing that what they are saying is worth backing. They improve their chances of achieving what they desire because they generate belief in others that builds momentum," he says.

"But not everyone has the ability to be like that," I offer, knowing that taking on such tasks is not within everyone's reach. "Sometimes we see and hear things we feel are wrong or that could be different, and we'd like to see a change, but, not everyone has the strength of conviction to create such changes."

"That's right; some people make change happen and some don't. But what is the difference between them, Tom; what is the difference between those who say 'I can' and those who *don't* say it?"

"I should have known it." I look away from him, somewhat dejectedly. "I should've kept my mouth shut, shouldn't I?" Again, he has asked one of his searching questions; the type of question I have no immediate answer to. "I don't know," I say coming back to face him. But he just keeps on looking back at me, almost as if he's waiting for me to think a little harder. "Oh I don't know; some people can't be bothered… It's too much like hard work… Or maybe because they think someone else will do it." I look back at him hoping for a reply, which doesn't come. I am out of ideas, so offer the last thing I can think of, "Because they think they can't influence things; they feel they can't make the change happen?"

"You see, the answer was there all along. Believing you can is half the battle, the rest is about your commitment to that belief and being willing to follow it through," he says with a wry smile. "The difference lies in what people *think*. The ones who say they can are the ones who *think* they can, because they tend to hear more positive thoughts."

"Sorry," I stop him. "What do you mean, *hear* more positive thoughts?"

"Let me explain," he says. "But bear with me as this may take a while."

"OK. I'll try."

"Every one has an internal voice which is in almost constant dialogue with them."

"Tell me about it!" I say, knowing how much I sometimes want to switch that voice off.

"Did you know that there are different types of internal dialogues though?" he asks.

"No, I wasn't aware of that. It all seems like one big loud voice to me. But then, I haven't been aware of most of your ideas up until now, have I?"

"That's why this is a valuable time for you. Opening up to these ideas takes courage along with a willingness to listen and reflect."

"I'm getting there," I say, admitting how uncomfortable this has been for me.

"Every journey is different," he says, with a reassuring smile. "So, when it comes to the internal dialogue it can be conscious, covert or unconscious," he brings us back on track.

"Go on," I say.

"The conscious dialogue is the one you hear most clearly. It is a chosen, purposeful conversation you have with yourself; it's a conscious internal dialogue about what you experience that helps you assess and arrive at decisions. Although I should stress that not all decisions are made at a conscious level."

"Really?" I ask, bemused by this bold statement.

"Yes. Remember, there are two other internal dialogues and they are just as influential, if not more."

"OK, carry on then."

"The covert is rarely at rest, it chats away commenting on people and situations and can be quite opinionated. It's the internal dialogue you notice you're having that seems to come from nowhere, the one you don't remember starting but which is now expressing itself. Sometimes it pops up and suggests ways forward or it comments on what you experience. It likes to offer suggestions, sometimes randomly, and has the potential to influence what you say and do."

"It sounds to me like conscious and covert are quite similar; what is the difference between them?"

"Conscious is exactly that, it's a *chosen* internal conversation. Whereas covert is not chosen, it comes in under the radar, so to speak. It's the kind of thing you notice yourself thinking and wonder where the thought came from."

"OK.," I say, just about understanding the concept. "So, what about the unconscious then, what's that all about?"

"The unconscious dialogue takes place at a deeper level; it doesn't offer itself up for conversation, instead it manipulates and manoeuvres below the surface. It speaks to your unconscious mind and to your instinct. You could say it likes to work behind closed doors, but it has the potential to be immensely powerful and influential."

The idea of the unconscious isn't new to me, but an unconscious dialogue is; I want to know more, "But do I hear this unconscious dialogue?"

"It is unlikely that you will hear it," he says. "Most of the time it lives up to its name; you are unconscious of it. But you can become aware of it after the fact. Once you are attuned to the idea of awareness you may start to notice things you did or said that were brought about by the unconscious dialogue's influence."

"Sounds to me like the covert and unconscious *both* influence things we say and do," I say, still slightly confused.

"Yes, they do. The difference between them is that with covert you become aware of it in the moment, whereas it's hindsight that helps you to recognise the unconscious dialogue's influence. Either way, once you become aware of their influence you have a choice; you either agree with their opinion and influence or you disagree and make a decision to change it."

"So, as you say, I *can* change my mind."

"Yes, *when* you become aware of your internal dialogue's influence. These dialogues are an important part of you; they affect the beliefs you have about yourself, other people and the things you encounter. They influence who you are and how you interact with the world around you."

"But do these dialogues actually represent me?" I ask, concerned that all my thoughts might actually be a part of who I am and what I believe.

"Just because you have a thought does not mean you are the thought, Tom. They may come from within, but they do not necessarily represent you. I am confident that you'll have had thoughts in your life, probably covert, which seem out of character; you question their validity or origin."

"Oh, you're not wrong there," I say. "That's why I'm asking. Some of the thoughts I have about people, especially ones I haven't actually met, seem to come from nowhere; they can be so off the wall, even inappropriate, they really catch me out. Sometimes I even stop for a second to wonder whether I actually believe the thought I just had."

"There you go. You just confirmed what we are talking about. You have *many* thoughts in a day, so many in fact, it is impossible to monitor just how many you have."

"Do we really have that many thoughts?" I ask.

"Oh yes. Let me show you."

"OK," I say, enthralled by what we might do now.

"Right; I'd like you to turn to sit comfortably in your seat and for thirty seconds I want you to do nothing. Just sit there, being still and relaxed; and during that time I want you to see if you can notice how many separate thoughts you have."

"Sounds a bit like meditation," I say, turning to face forward in the bench.

"Yes, in a way, it is," he says. "Have you tried that?"

"Oh yes, I've tried it. But *try* is the operative word. I've never been able to switch my….." I stop mid sentence and turn back to face Gabriel. "I've never been able to switch my mind off!" I exclaim.

"So, you struggle to switch off your internal dialogues! But have you ever been *close* to switching them off?" he asks.

I hesitate, not sure if I've actually ever been able to meditate successfully. "I think I've been able to switch it off for moments. But that's all they were. Because sure enough, I always start thinking about something, a thought always comes in just when I think I've switched my mind off."

"And can you explain why you have all these thoughts?"

"No, not all of them," I say, baffled by the idea of working this out. Surely they come from within. "My mind seems a pretty active place, now I come to think of it."

"There you are. There is a steady flow of thoughts streaming through you all the time; and, as you've identified, they don't all represent you. They are just thoughts. Because you think something does not mean you believe it. But, what happens when a thought *becomes* a belief, Tom?"

"Well, then I act out of it," I say, hoping I have the right answer, but sounding a little unsure, given how many times he's caught me out on things like this before.

"Exactly. That is why we are talking about belief. If you believe in something you are more inclined to take action based on it. But, given the number of thoughts floating around inside wanting to have their say, the art lies in knowing when to listen and when to filter."

Again, he's entering unexplored territory for me. "Help me out again, I'm not quite with you."

"The art lies in being able to recognise the ones which are useful for you, the ones you believe are representational of you," he leans forward. "Imagine you were able to read people's minds, would you do it all the time?" he asks, looking intrigued as to how I might answer.

"Ooh, now that's a good question!" I take in a steady breath as I consider my reply. For sure, being able to read people's minds would be great, I'd have such fun learning what people really think. But, now I'm being asked to consider being able to do it, I realise just how invasive and inappropriate it could be. "No," I reply. "I don't think I'd do it *all* the time. There'd be too much to hear; I'd have to try and work out what was worth listening to."

"Exactly. If you could read people's minds and didn't know how to control it, there'd be a constant noise in your head. Imagine what you hear as the spoken word when you are in the company of others and multiply it a hundred fold, that goes close to what you would experience. You'd learn to not listen all the time; you'd have to find a way to filter what you choose to pay attention to. Thankfully you don't have that dilemma!" he says, sending me a smile. "So it is with the internal dialogue. You tune in and filter out what is worth paying attention to. That is what essentially differentiates the people who say they can and the ones who don't. They are good at listening selectively, asking if what they hear is representational or useful and they choose which thoughts to filter out."

"But that sounds like they are only ever looking for the positive. Is that what you're asking me to do?" I ask.

"No, that is not what I am saying. By all means search out the positive, because being positive will certainly help you achieve the changes you seek. But my message here is: seek out the thoughts which are *worth* exploring. Sometimes negative thoughts are worth exploring; especially when they help you assess if something is realistic or not, if something is not achievable or a bad idea. If you recognise the negative thoughts when you have them and question their validity, you move away from being at the affect of a negative downward spiral. Unchallenged negative thoughts tend to nurture further negative thoughts. Too many people have negative thoughts, accept them at face value without challenging them and ultimately end up unconsciously acting out of them. However, the 'I can' people hear the negative and question whether it is appropriate and something they are willing to accept or not," he stops to check I am still following him. "Remember when we were sitting in the library talking about awareness for the first time?"

"Yes," I say, just about hanging onto the flow of his ideas.

"You started talking about your divorce being a foregone conclusion and I asked if that were really the case."

"Yes," I say, curious about the shift in topic.

"In that moment I was merely asking you to question your negative dialogue, to see if it were truly the case and whether you were willing to challenge that perception. If you believe it's over, then it is; but if you're willing to challenge that belief and to stand in the face of what you recognise as a negative situation, you might be able to do something to change it. If, that is, you are interested in changing it."

"I see." Having it applied to my situation directly helps me understand his idea better.

"Now come back to where this particular conversation started, Tom; with the statement that those who say they can, *think* they can. It comes down to whether you *believe* something or not."

I hold back from commenting straight away, digesting what he's just said. There's no doubting it, right now I am having a conscious dialogue. "Wow! You make it sound so straight forward, Gabriel; but, I've got to say, it also sounds like it could take a lot of effort to get to that point."

"Yes it can, and creating change can be uncomfortable. But, if you have enough desire around creating change, if you start to believe in that change, it's my observation that barriers and obstacles to achieving it tend to either move or are easier to overcome. Belief is powerful, Tom. Change requires energy and that energy comes from desire and belief."

"You weren't wrong, that certainly did take a bit of explaining," I say, feeling quite drained by the depth of our conversation and keen for some respite. Would you mind if we took a break? We've been talking a long time."

"Of course we can. It's time for you to rest anyway and absorb what we've been discussing," he says, leaning back in his pew. With that the church fades as everything turns to the familiar safe white space; and as my consciousness drifts I hear him say, "be aware of the negative mind, Tom; it will challenge you along your journey to creating change. Be stronger than it; search for the positive."

Letting Go

I am woken by the rhythmical sound of waves unfolding lazily against a shore; freeing themselves from the sea momentarily before being dragged back homewards. As I listen to the heartbeat of the sea, my breath synchronises with its gentle pattern, in and out. Then I notice a warmth caressing my feet; from tip of toe to ankle and back again. I open my eyes and look down to see waves lapping around and over my feet. They mesmerise me as I find myself drawn to the harmony of their constant motion and sound.

Lifting my eyes I see I am sat at the edge of a pale sandy beach facing out over a vast stretch of water. Ahead of me the sun flickers along its softly undulating surface. As much as the rhythm of the waves is constant, the water stretching ahead of me barely moves beyond a ripple. I hear it, feel it on my feet, see it ahead and smell the clean salty air as I inhale what can only be described as tranquillity into the pit of my stomach. I am at one with the sea, and with myself. I close my eyes again and wallow in the sensation, my shoulders relaxing downwards, all traces of tension gone.

For the first time in as long as I can remember, nothing matters to me. I want to keep this moment pure, to sustain this peaceful state. If it were possible for me to stop time to savour this moment, I would do. This is precisely what I have endeavoured to find on the occasions I've tried meditating. My mind is quiet, I feel no need to be anywhere or do anything, other than just be here. So many times my mind has fought me, talked at me, told me what to do or nagged me to have a conversation with it about something. Gabriel was right, my mind has always wanted to have a *dialogue* with me; but right now that dialogue is turned right down. My mind is working *with* me, doing nothing except be with the sound of the waves.

The sun warms me as my heart falls in line with the soothing waves. I could stay like this forever; but the memory of the sun dappled expanse of water ahead entices me to open my eyes again. The sea bounces the bright sun off like a fractured mirror reflecting shards of light. The expanse of water fills my vision. I turn to see how far it stretches along the beach and notice another pair of feet next to me in the water. "Morning," comes Gabriel's dulcet voice.

I take a steady breath in, filling my lungs with the sea air and lift my head to face him with a smile of contentment. "Morning Gabriel," I say, my voice barely above a whisper. We look into each other, not needing to say anything as we share our moment sitting at the edge of the sea, the warm waves lapping our feet.

"It's relaxing isn't it?" he says, breaking the silence, prompting me to gaze away again at the sea. "Hmmm," I offer in barely audible agreement.

Suddenly my mind flicks back into a very conscious dialogue: surely he can't have spoken just then as he didn't move his lips. But he did speak, I distinctly heard him. Did he just say that or did I think it? I'm sure his lips didn't move. But I swear I heard him speak... Wait a minute... Did he just speak to me telepathically? I turn to look back at him and scan his face for signs of anything to help me. Nah, surely...

"See what can happen if you switch your mind off. Other things are allowed the possibility of being!" he says, and this time I can see he is speaking to me.

I'm really taken aback by this; not only is he confirming that he spoke to me without moving his lips; he's telling me how it was possible. This is too much to take in one go. "Hold on a minute..." I put my hand up to stop him, but also as an act to stop the moment so I can at least try to grasp hold of what has just happened. "Are you telling me that you just read my mind?... And that you can speak to me telepathically?"

"Yes," comes his simple, spoken, reply.

"H...How....?" The word struggles to come out. I want to ask how he's able to do it, but am incapable of saying anything else.

"Again, you judge what I can do by what you have become accustomed to knowing and understanding. I remind you, there are other possibilities. It's surprising what it is possible to let in when you let go," he replies.

By now my mind is whirring; this is amazing. How is someone able to do what he's just done? Am I capable of doing it? Are we all capable of it? Have people been reading my mind before when I wasn't aware? A series of thoughts and questions compete for attention.

"Relax, Tom. Very few people in your world are able to do what I just did, and, I am afraid, you are not one of them. But, yes, I can read your mind, if I choose to. And I can talk to you that way too. You were able to hear me just now because your mind was quiet; the chatter that would normally get in the way of you hearing me was not there," he says, making it sound as normal as could be, even logical that this was possible.

But his answer only stirs me on to another question, "Can *I* learn to do it?"

"I am afraid the answer is 'No'," he says, with a warmth only he is capable of mustering while letting someone down.

"But..." I interject. "I was able to hear you, wasn't I? Surely that means I can learn?"

"You were able to hear me because your mind was spinning slow enough to allow me in, so I could place my voice inside your mind."

"Spinning? What do you mean by that?" I ask, caught out by another of his phrases.

"Do you remember when we talked about the internal dialogue?"

"Yes."

"Well, spin is the pace at which you process or rotate thoughts in your mind. If you're spinning too fast, it's difficult to let other things in. Let me give you a picture of how it works. Imagine you were in your car waiting to enter a busy roundabout, but there was lots of traffic, all moving round too fast; you would struggle to enter the flow of traffic. However, if there were less traffic or it was moving slower, you'd be able to enter more easily. So it is with the rate you spin your thoughts. Too fast and it's difficult for anything else to enter. Slow it down and there is room for something else to be heard. Just now you had slowed your thoughts down so much that there was ample space for me to slip into your consciousness and for you to hear me."

"Wow!" Again he has explained something in such a way that it makes perfect sense, when it's actually so far away from what I know and understand. "So, if I slow down my rate of thoughts, I can hear you?"

"Yes; because your mind is ready to hear."

"So, how do I listen to others then?" I ask, keen to learn more.

He looks at me as if he's weighing up whether or not to tell me the truth and assessing which will be the easiest way to say it. "You were able to hear me because I placed my voice inside your mind and I was only able to do that because your mind was spinning slower. I'm afraid to say, though, that just because you heard me does not mean that you will be able to listen to others or speak to their minds."

"But you did say that some people are able to do it; didn't you?" I push further, eager for him to concede and tell me that there is a way to learn, if I apply myself.

"Do you think you are you the same as everyone else, Tom?" he asks.

"Well…" I hesitate, not sure of what he's actually asking. "Of course we are all different, because we're uniquely individual; but on the other hand, yes I am the same as other people. On a fundamental level we're all essentially the same; we all have a body, a brain, eyes…" I reel my list off, animated in my effort to convince him I have what it takes. "We may have differences, but essentially we have the same things. We share many commonalities; like the fact that the majority of us speak, even though we sound different. I know some people can't speak, but the majority of us share that ability because we are basically the same physical beings," I say, convinced that by being the same in such ways means we share the ability to do things equally.

"You do share many of these commonalities; in essence you're right, you are the same. But, as you say, equally each of you is different. Let me give you an example: the vast majority of you share an ability to do mathematics, but you've surely noticed how some have the ability to excel?" I nod my acknowledgement. "Have you also noticed how some people are better musicians than others, while some may be better at sports?"

"Yes," I nod again, confused as to how this is significant.

"Talent, skill and ability are specific to the person. In that respect, each of you goes in the direction your skills and strengths enable you to go; you all have individual strengths and abilities. Yes, you share being human, but you don't share everything. Just because some are able to do something or excel at it does not mean that *all* are able to."

"Ah, but when it comes down to the basics, we are the same. Our anatomy is the same; the dynamic of who we are is the same. Look at how we've developed as people, we've evolved as a race, we've learned together; we've grown together because we are the same essentially. We have the ability to learn new ways; surely, therefore, most of us have the ability to learn whatever it was you just did? I mean, if I can hear you, then surely I have the basics to work on?" I finish, looking straight at him, convinced of my argument.

"You certainly do have the ability to learn new ways, that is what I've been talking about with you since we first met; but this is not one of those things. This is different to, say, learning to walk, or learning a new language. Let us go back to the idea of an athlete. Imagine you wanted to be a world class athlete; that you wanted to win a gold medal at the Olympics, just like Sophie did at the Paralympics. Do you think you could win gold in any sport you chose to?"

I have to think about that one for a second. "Yes. I think so. If I chose the right sport and worked hard at it; yes I could win. We're often told that we can do anything we set our mind to."

"And do you believe that?"

I hesitate, about to speak but each time stopping before creating a full word as I process a list of possible answers. Surely this is what so many books and motivational speakers tell us, that we *are* capable of achieving just about anything we set our mind to. Then the penny drops as I hear myself play back what I just thought: 'capable of *just about* anything'. I break my gaze away from Gabriel and look out over the sea, the warm waves still lapping around my feet. I'm confused. I turn back to him. "Well, we can do *just about anything* we set our mind to."

"Yes, you are capable of achieving many things, especially if you set your mind to it; but not everything, Tom. While you may be an able bodied person, with two arms and legs, you can hear, see and you are fit; do you think it possible that you could have won the gold medal at the Olympic 100 metre sprint?" he asks, looking eager to know my answer.

"Oh come on, Gabriel. You are of course joking. Look at me; not only am I in a coma, I'm *too old* for that kind of thing now."

"I'm not asking if you could do it now. I'm asking if you believe you could have won it at an earlier stage in your life? Given you have, as you say, the same as everyone else," he says, with a hint of sarcasm, as he repeats my earlier words.

As much as I was quite athletic at school I never won a sprint race, I didn't have the speed for it. I was much better at the middle distances; I had better stamina for that kind of race. "Not the 100 metres, no. It wasn't my kind of race," I admit. "But if it were the 1500 metres, now that's different; maybe if I'd wanted it enough and trained hard at it, yes I suppose it could have been possible."

"So, if you developed enough desire to win and nurtured a belief in your ability, you are telling me you could have won at the 1500 metres?" he asks.

"Yes. Now that we're talking my kind of race, it's possible," I say, a little taken aback at my own words; given I've never thought about competing at the Olympics, let alone the possibility of winning.

"So, what you are saying, then, is that you are better suited to win certain races than others; is that right?"

Again, I am confused as to where he's taking me with his line of questions. I try to come up with something clever to say, but realise there is only one answer available. "Yes," I admit.

"And so it is with many things. You choose according to the abilities you have, you play to your strengths. In the case we've just been talking about, you choose the sport which gives you the best chance of winning. But you have to be realistic in making sure that what you set out to achieve is something you are capable of achieving. Would you agree?"

"Yes. As usual you're right," I concede, somewhat dejectedly.

"Knowing where your strengths and abilities lie, accepting the truth about that and choosing your way based on that knowledge, gives you a better chance of achieving what you want." He holds my gaze as I digest what he's just said. "So it is that not everyone has the ability to listen or speak to other's minds, Tom."

He's done it again. He's managed to put his point across so well that I have to accept defeat in this debate. "Ah well, it was a nice thought," I say, resigned to the fact that I'm won't be able to read minds.

"Well you did say that you wouldn't want to read people's minds all the time, so perhaps it is just as well," he offers, with a cheeky air of consolation.

"It would've been good to have learnt that one though. But I guess we all have to accept the limits of our own capabilities," I say, turning to look back out to sea.

"That is right, Tom. Notice how you used the idea of acceptance just then. Acceptance is crucial to recognising what has been; but also what *is* and what *can* be. Be in the moment, accept what comes and choose your way," he says, leaving silence to follow. I look back at him, my attention caught. "Allowing yourself to be in the moment gives you the best chance to sense what the moment offers – the truth! As I have already mentioned, recognising, naming and accepting the truth can be powerful. If you stay in the moment and accept the truth that comes, you are in a much better position to choose your way forward."

The sound of waves escaping the sea and being sucked back continues as Gabriel's words linger in my mind, 'be in the moment, accept what comes and choose your way'. My internal dialogue talks to me about the uncomfortable truth of the predicament I find myself in. "It's not always easy to accept what comes though, is it?" I offer, still looking out to sea.

"No, acceptance is seldom easy. But recognise what you have achieved during our time together; you have absorbed the idea of acceptance very well. The art lies in trying to accept what comes in each moment, being *willing* to accept the truth each moment brings."

I hear what he says, but battle with the emotions this particular moment is bringing up for me. Coming to terms with the truth of this moment has to be the biggest acceptance going; that I might be dead, that life might be over. "But, the truth isn't always easy to hear, let alone accept... In fact," I turn to look back at him, "it can be downright hard sometimes."

"Go on," he says, encouraging me to say what is lurking beneath.

"The fact that I don't know if I'm going to live... Or die." This time it's my words left lingering in the air, mixing with the sound of the waves. "That's a truth that's not easy to accept!" I say, lowering my head to look at my hands as a lump returns to my throat.

"It is the most difficult of all truths to accept... But be with *this* moment, Tom... Being in a coma has allowed you to spend time here, to have these conversations. You have shown a great deal of grace in accepting your time with me," his voice sounds as close to me as if he were speaking softly into my ear.

"Really?" I say, turning slowly to look at him. "Because it doesn't feel like it!"

"Yes. You are accepting your situation very well. From where I am sitting you have stopped fighting and denying. You seem to have accepted where you are in your life right now," his voice consoles me as he speaks.

"But I don't know my way forward," I say, my voice barely above a whisper. "How can I... 'choose my way'... if I don't know what my options are?" My entire world is still, focused solely on Gabriel's face.

"Right now you are 'in the moment' more than you have ever been. Try to stay with the truth of this moment. You are here because of your life to date. Do nothing more than accept what this moment brings you. Choose that and nothing more," he holds my gaze before carrying on. "Your struggle comes because you are trying to look ahead, trying to foretell the future; to know whether you will go back or not. Choose to be here, Tom," his voice a delicate encouraging tone. "Be in *this* moment; accept the truth of *this* moment."

I search for what to say as my stomach churns trying to avoid the truth of this moment. "But what about 'choosing my way'?" I ask, expressing my confusion. "Isn't that part of your idea? Isn't that what comes next?"

"Your only option is to choose being here. *This* is where you are. *This* is your truth. Accept that your own actions have brought you here; be with the truth of this moment; not knowing what comes next."

I look out to sea, transfixed by the sun reflecting across its surface; the silence of this powerful moment punctuated only by the sound of waves breaking over each other, coating the beach beneath my feet. The fight inside me wanes as I hear Gabriel's words play over in my head and come to terms with what he's asking of me. "OK," I whisper. "I don't like it; but I accept what you are saying."

"It is hard to let go of something when you are still attached to it," he softly offers.

"Yeah," I mutter. And for the first time since meeting Gabriel, a tear trickles down my cheek.

"Keep breathing, Tom. Follow the rhythm of the waves and be with your moment. You are all right. Let go of whatever you need to let go of and let your truth in." His voice seems to be inside my head again, but I have no idea how he's talking to me and right now, I don't care. There is a steady flow of tears now, but not the torrent I might've expected. Gabriel is right, this is the truth of my moment and I'm allowing myself to accept what comes. Strangely my emotions are a mix of sadness and what I can only describe as a form of happiness at accepting the truth of where I am in my life. I'm confused by what I'm feeling, but decide to just allow rather than analyse or understand my thoughts and feelings. The tears keep coming, dripping off my nose and chin onto my feet; the waves washing them away as they come one after the other.

I have no idea how much time passes before Gabriel speaks again, "To let in new possibilities, you must be willing to let go of what was, Tom."

"Yeah!" I say, with sheer acceptance of what he's offering; no questions, no hesitation, just acceptance. The idea of being in the moment and accepting what comes resonates soundly for me now.

He continues, "In order to move forward it is important to let go of what was. If you hold on to things from the past they have the potential to drag you back. Like an anchor dragging along the sea bed stops a boat from going in the direction you desire.

"Notice how when one wave has finished another comes to take its place? It never stops, the ebb and flow of waves is constant. When the sun sets, night comes, the dark follows light; but sure enough next day the light returns. These are constants. You must let day go and accept night, in order that day may once again come in the morning. When one thing ends so another begins. Life is full of such constants; life is full of change. When you stop being in the world, it will keep on turning, day will follow night and one wave will replace another. Change is constant, Tom, and the future is created moment to moment by the choices you make. Be in the moment, accept what comes and choose your way."

I hear every word he says clearly, each one finding a place to rest somewhere in me; yet I have nothing to offer in reply. Indeed there seems little I can offer back, other than a willingness to be in the moment with him, each wave washing our feet; the sea stretching ahead of us.

"Take a rest Tom." And before I can even think of answering, quicker than on any of the previous occasions, the scene pales away and I drift into a state of nothingness as if the switch lighting my world had been turned off. My mind recognises and welcomes the state of oblivion that follows.

Time to Choose

Stirring from the deepest state of rest since meeting Gabriel, the first thing I notice is the smell of fresh coffee. I take in a long and steady breath, allowing its evocative aroma to sooth the contours of my mind. Though I am fully conscious, I keep my eyes closed, enjoying the calming sensation, my shoulders drooped as if stroked into place. Beyond the smell of coffee I make out a gentle murmur of people chatting, which grows with intensity, lifting me out of my reverie and encouraging me to engage with wherever I have been brought this time. My eyelids part, gradually allowing light in; and the first thing I see is Gabriel sitting across from me on a large comfortable looking leather sofa, a low wooden table separating us. His head is turned away to the left and I automatically follow his gaze to see a room full of people either sitting at tables or in comfy chairs and sofas. It quickly becomes apparent that, as the smell had suggested, we are in a coffee shop. Further to the left a queue of people wait at the counter, some looking around for a place to sit, others buying drinks and leaving with cardboard cups in hand. The staff behind the counter are as active as bees in a hive, milling around offering smiles to their customers as they take their orders and offer them drinks.

"Hello Tom," comes Gabriel's familiar voice from in front of me, pulling me back to focus on him.

"Hello!" I chirp back. It's almost as if the conversation on the beach has cleansed me, as I feel wide eyed and perky. Not only am I refreshed after my rest, but the smell of coffee has woken me in a jolly mood. Then I notice a rather large cappuccino sitting in front of me on the table, topped with an ample sprinkling of cocoa powder. "Ooh, lovely. Is that for me?" I ask, my eyes widening further.

"Yes."

I lean forward from my sumptuous leather sofa and wrap my fingers around the mug of coffee. Its warmth spreads through my hands as I pick it up, my eyes fixed on the cocoa. Lifting it toward me, I hold the mug just below my nose for a few seconds, closing my eyes again to savour the aroma of my first coffee in far too long. Then, opening my eyes, I tilt the mug towards my mouth and take my first sip. Just how I like it: strong, sweet, with the taste of the froth adding a comforting creamy tone. I roll the flavours around my mouth, my tongue tracing along the inside of my teeth. The mug hovers inches away from my mouth as I savour the experience. "Mmmm!" I give a satisfied moan of delight. "That tastes good!" Then draw it back up for another taste. "Thank you, that's a lovely cup of coffee," I say, place the mug back on the table and lean back into my sofa utterly satisfied, a sense I haven't felt in a long time.

"Good. I'm glad you like that. It is nice to have some creature comforts every now and then. For me, it's a cup of hot chocolate topped with cream and marshmallows," he says, leaning forward to pick up his mug and take a sip. There is so much whipped cream atop his hot chocolate that as he takes the mug away from his mouth to place it back on the table again, a trace of cream is left on the tip of his nose.

"You've... erm.... got a bit of... erm," I say, pointing to the tip of my own nose as I speak. Gabriel looks back at me somewhat bemused. "Cream!" I finish, still pointing to my own nose.

"Oh, thank you," he acknowledges with a smile, wiping the cream from his nose before sucking it off his finger.

"What happens if someone wants to sit here? I ask, genuinely concerned we might have a tricky moment ahead of us, "I mean, this is a busy place and if people can't see us they're going to try to sit on these sofas aren't they?"

"Oh, this is different, Tom. They can sense we are here, they see people sitting in these sofas, but nothing more. If someone were asked to describe us, what we did or what we said they would not be able to recall a thing about us. You must have seen thousands of people just like that in your lifetime; people you have seen but not seen?"

"Yeah, I guess I have, even though I don't remember. So, is that how we are seen by these people then?" I indicate using my thumb, still trying not to be too obvious.

"Yes. How do you think I was able to buy these drinks?" he says, his eyes widening as he nods towards the counter and queue of people.

"You mean you didn't... *magic* these drinks up?" I ask.

"No, not this time. I like getting directly involved sometimes."

"Yes, but Gabriel, you're *just a little bit* different from other people," I say, with a hint of sarcasm in my voice. "You do tend to, well, stick out a bit!"

"Not when I don't want to," he replies, passing me one of his playful looks across the coffee table."

"I know!" I say, lifting my hand to indicate that he need not say another word; it isn't worth questioning how he's able to do these things anymore. "You're just able to do it and I shouldn't try to compare your world with the world I've become accustomed to. Thanks for the coffee anyway, it's a really nice thought. So, why are we here Gabriel?"

"Because I want you to observe people," he says, looking around the place again.

"OK. But haven't we kind of been doing that already?" I ask light heartedly. "I mean, there've been people at most of the places we've been to."

"There is a lot to be learned from looking, Tom. And each time you look it is possible to see different things. Sometimes what you are looking for determines what you see," he replies, with one of his knowing looks.

"So, what are we looking for then?"

"Be patient," he says, leaning forward to have another drink of hot chocolate; this time leaving no cream on his nose. "All we have discussed so far and everything you have experienced on your journey with me has led to this point."

I hesitate, my eyes scanning the room trying to work out the significance of the coffee shop. Every place he's taken me to before has had a relevance to whatever we talked about, so why here? Why has everything been leading to *this* point? "So what's special about this place then?" I ask, unable to fathom an answer for myself.

"Oh there is nothing special about the coffee shop; I just thought you might like a cup of coffee while we take stock of your journey so far. I thought you might like to relax as we discuss this next stage."

"So, what is *this* stage?" I ask, recognising by now the part I play in drawing information from him.

"This is where you choose," he says calmly, awarding a level of importance to the final word.

At last! He's given me something to go on; but, as usual, he's also left me needing to know more. "Choose what?"

"If you want things to be different," he says, his eyes conveying an intensity I haven't seen before.

"But haven't we already covered this, on the beach?"

"*Have* you chosen, Tom?"

The word 'yes' lingers in my mind. I want to answer him, but confusion mingles with uncertainty; too many times before he's caught me out with his clever questioning and so now I'm not sure how to answer. Have I misunderstood what happened on the beach? What is he actually asking me this time?

"It is possible to get to this point and do nothing," he carries on. "It is possible to get to this point and be satisfied at just having had the conversation with yourself. But unless you decide to make something *be* different, it will not necessarily happen; you must *choose* to make it happen. And, in doing so, you may need to break with existing, sometimes deeply rooted, beliefs or agreements."

Now he has me caught like a fish on a hook, "Go on."

"Your beliefs are the agreements you have made with yourself in response to your experiences." He leaves another silence as I lean forward to pick up my mug and take another sip; digesting his words as the coffee warms its way down to my stomach. "You were born with certain thought patterns and ways of being already programmed in; what you might refer to as genetics. But you were not born with any beliefs; your mind was blank in that respect. As I said when we were in the church, you acquire beliefs. You were born with an inquisitive mind, a mind that wants to learn; indeed it has an almost insatiable appetite."

At last there's something for me to latch onto, a subject close to my heart. Emily is now a lively eight year old girl, with an alert, inquisitive mind. As a baby she'd been eager to observe, learn, absorb and take in information, to assimilate. Sometimes this had been so obvious to me, I swear I'd seen her witness something and make an assessment; almost as if I could see cogs whirring in her head as she processed what she was watching. "Yes, Emily was like that as a baby, it's almost as if sometimes I could see her developing. Actually," I smile, "she does it now; she still asks questions, she's still eager to learn," I beam as I feel my love for her well up inside. How could there ever have been any doubt about my love and commitment to Emily? She means the world to me and facing the very real possibility of never seeing her again reminds me of the absolute nature of my predicament.

"Are you alright?" Gabriel asks, sincere concern in his eyes. He looks for all intents and purposes that he is willing to stop going in the direction of my discomfort and, for once, to ease off; maybe take a break from his relentless efforts to get me to understand the intricacies of our conversations.

Realising there is nowhere else for me to be right now other than in the moment I am in and knowing that I just need to accept my position, I shrug off the surge of emotion and choose to stay with the conversation and carry on. "I miss her," I say. "I regret some of how I've been with her; but, as you have helped me understand, this is where I am now, this is what I have created. It's painful sometimes, taking responsibility; not just for one's own actions but for the consequences."

He says nothing in response, allowing me to reflect. All the while his eyes send a very clear message that he is with me, supporting and caring for me.

If things had been different at work, I wouldn't have been planning to go to Bahrain and I wouldn't have been driving as I was in the fog; the accident wouldn't have happened. I would've been seeing Emily this weekend and I could have shown her how much I do care for her. I could have proved Louise wrong. Then I realise what a worthless conversation this is to be having with myself, because things are as they are; work *was* that way, I *was* driving that way and the accident *did* happen. I am here with Gabriel and that is that. I can do nothing to change that, so I may as well stop going down this route and accept what I created. While these discussions with him have been confusing and painful at times, they have also been enlightening and have helped me see things with a different set of eyes. A trace of remorse has just shown itself and I realise now that I feel what I do because I love Emily and I miss her. My remorse is because the truth has come up to bite me. Accepting loss is hard and a self imposed loss is even worse.

"You see why this is an important stage?" Gabriel breaks my thoughts.

"Yes; I do," I say, almost pleased that he has stopped my internal dialogue.

"Why do you think the early years of a child are referred to as their *formative* years?" he returns immediately to the subject we were talking about. "Because the person is being formed by what they see, hear, feel, touch and sense; by what they experience. Would you agree?"

"Yes," I say, remembering how Emily had been in those formative years and reconnecting with the conversation. "It's wonderful to watch them absorb life, eager to suck in as much as they can."

"That is why every parent and adult has such a great responsibility," he says, sitting forward in his chair.

"Oh you're not wrong there." He's tapped into an easy conversation with me this time as it echoes well with my experience as a father. "Every parent is duty bound to be responsible."

"So what does that mean?" he asks.

"Well, we have a duty to bring a child up in a safe environment, to love our children and do for them the best we can, to educate them and teach them, to care for them, to give them the best possible start in life..." I hesitate, wondering whether I have been a good parent in that respect, a responsible parent.

"Emily is a beautiful and graceful child, you have done well, Tom; after all, who ever told you how to be a parent?" he says. Has he read my mind again?

"Well enough people are certainly willing to offer their opinion on how to be a parent and of course there are post-natal classes. But, yes, you're right; Louise and I learned how to be parents by trial and error." I take another sip of coffee as I recall how we learned by the seat of our pants sometimes. "Have I really done OK with Emily, though? I'm not so sure, what with the divorce proceedings... Sometimes I think she was quite forgotten about; and with me being so busy at work it's not always been possible to be there for her," I admit. These words come easily for me now; I wonder what Louise would think if she could hear me talking like this. She's been saying these things to me for some time, but it's only because I've spent time with Gabriel that I'm able to recognise and say it.

"You've done well; don't be hard on yourself. Of course, if you would like to make some changes to how you are with Emily, you could always choose to make it different," he offers with one of his smiles.

"Can I?" Gabriel has gone out of his way to make it clear he has no influence over whether I will return to live and he's steered wide of making any references that could lead me down a specific route. But accepting my position doesn't stop me wanting to know about my future, especially as he's now talking about the possibility of me changing how I am with Emily. "Oh please tell me I'm going back. I'd really like to make some changes."

"You know my answer to that, Tom. Rest assured, though, when the time is right, you will know."

This conversation leads me to a strange anomaly. On the one hand I think I'm coming to terms with my predicament, with the possibility that I might not go back to live. On the other, as our conversations have built I find I want to carry on living more and more; I want to go back, I want to be given the chance to do things differently. There is no question about it, my time with Gabriel is the most informative in my life. In fact, talk about a child's formative years, my time here is *transformative*.

"Let us see what time brings shall we?" Gabriel offers. "As much as we have talked about taking responsibility for what happens in your life, sometimes you just need to be open to the possibilities of what life itself will bring your way. There is a reason why people don't get to know when they die in advance; it allows them to live their lives. Keep on living what you have, Tom."

"You call this *living*?" I blurt out, shocking myself at how abrupt I am.

"Why are you frustrated?" he asks, calmly.

"Well… Just when I think I'm getting better at accepting,

something comes along to challenge me. Just when I think I'm doing OK, a new emotion pops up and knocks me for six... Come on, Gabriel, you've got to admit that talking about me *living what I have* is bound to challenge me. I know it's not your intention, but it's as if you are poking fun when you say something like that. And sure enough, when you said it, bang, up comes my frustration at not knowing."

"I understand. It is entirely natural that you should feel frustrated, even angry. But remember, very few people are given the opportunity to experience *this* journey," he says, opening his arms to indicate everything I've experienced with him so far. "You are one of the fortunate. Do not give up; be in this moment, accept *whatever* comes. Do not judge or be harsh on yourself."

"Yeah!!" I say, massaging my forehead, holding back the urge to point out what I've said so many times before: that accepting my position in no way equates to it being easy or comfortable to accept. "That's easier said than done though, Gabriel."

The silence that follows lasts for what seems like minutes, as my mind wanders on a different journey, playing out some of the events and circumstances that have happened in my life. Events and circumstances that ultimately led to me being here with Gabriel. And all the while he sits opposite me doing nothing; just being himself, caring for me with his eyes as I trace my own thoughts back and forth. Resigned to my situation, I pick up my mug, take another sip of my by now warm rather than hot coffee and lift my head to meet his eyes. "Hey, if I hadn't lived my life the way I had, I wouldn't have met you. I wouldn't be here with you now would I? I wouldn't have known any different." He just looks back at me, giving nothing away. "I guess with knowledge comes responsibility." I acknowledge.

He gives an almost imperceptible nod. "You are right, knowledge does come with responsibility." We hold a moment together, our eyes speaking a language that few people have the courage to share, a language born out of sharing the truth with someone else. Then, breaking that moment, he carries on; "So, parents have a great deal of responsibility."

"Yes," I agree; coming back a little shaken from what we've just talked about. "Sorry!" I offer, acknowledging my frustration on the shifting conversation.

"No apology needed. It shows you care," his eyebrows lift briefly, before carrying on. "There is, however, a level of responsibility that not all parents, indeed not all adults, realise."

"Go on, where are you going this time?" I ask.

"The responsibility to allow the child's mind to develop freely," he leaves another pause which I'm unable to fill as I struggle to comprehend. "The child learns a lot from what adults pass on. The child is a willing vessel, eager to absorb and learn, even eager to be accepted and loved by those around them. Each child is individual, as indeed we have established all people are, and as the child grows up it learns to express its individuality. The mind finds a way of expressing its own thoughts, its own identity."

"Well, yes, I suppose so. Emily certainly had her own character and wanted to exert her way of being from a very early age. I can remember times when it seemed as though she and I were in a battle of wills," I say, recalling the many times she had tried to convince me that her way was the right way.

"Being able to express your individuality is part of what makes you human, it is present from birth and an important part of your development. But, would you agree, there comes a time when the child appears to independently make decisions about what it deems right or wrong, what it believes?"

This sparks a memory for me; "Yes, I remember when Emily first expressed an opinion she'd arrived at by herself; it quite caught me out at the time. We were out for a walk in the park and had seen a boy being told off for trying to kick a dog. Instead of asking why he was being told off she commented that she thought it was wrong for the boy to kick the dog and that he should know better. I remember agreeing with her outwardly, but inwardly I was full of pride. Actually it took me a moment to reply as I was taking in what had just happened more than thinking about a reply."

"Was she expressing her opinion or yours though?"

I have no hesitation; "Oh it was her own. She arrived at that opinion by herself; I didn't say anything to influence her."

"Are you sure about that?"

"Yes, I am. She thought it for herself and expressed what she thought. That was what caught me out. You see she'd never expressed an opinion other than things like what she wanted to eat or what she wanted to watch on telly before. I may have said that hurting animals was wrong at some point as she was growing up, but she had that thought on seeing someone try to hurt a dog and then she chose to express it. I never said anything to influence her or make her say anything; what she said was spontaneous."

"And that highlights what I'm saying about responsibility."

"Highlights what? I'm afraid you've lost me," I say, somewhat irritated by his statement.

"Emily probably chose to express that thought because at some point in the past she had been told that it was wrong to hurt animals."

"Yeah, well, OK…. I get that idea…… But how is that such a big thing, Gabriel? It seems pretty obvious to me that hurting an animal is wrong and children should be taught not to do it." I'm confused by where he's going with this.

"I agree with you; hurting animals is wrong. What I am alluding to is that a lot of what children learn in their formative years, as they grow up, comes from the adults around them; from those who already have their own thoughts, opinions and beliefs. Adults pass these on to children, sometimes unconsciously, and often influence them into agreeing with them. Because the child is inquisitive, it wants to take on board ideas and so it absorbs what adults offer, probing and looking for more all the time."

"Hence the 'Why' question that all children seem to have programmed into them," I interrupt, thinking I've made sense of what he's just said.

"That's right. Children have inquisitive minds, so they want to know *why* they should take on board an idea offered by an adult. However, the adult usually believes they are right in whatever they are conveying to the child, so they reinforce their idea with arguments that the child can understand and easily take on board," he remains his usual calm, measured self. "In effect, they *sell* their idea in such a way as it becomes attractive for the child to buy."

Recognising some of what he is talking about, I jump in again. "And when the adult doesn't have an answer to back up their idea, that's when we revert to the 'because I say so!' answer."

"Yes," comes his simple answer, with the look of someone who understands the parents frustration at constantly being asked questions by a child.

"But where are you going with this conversation?" I ask.

"Many things adults teach children are appropriate, even necessary; such as your example about not hurting the dog. The point I am making here is that it is also possible for the adult to pass on other beliefs to the child."

"OK, but what sort of beliefs do you mean?"

"Well, humans are rather opinionated and often prone to wanting to convince others that their opinions are right. So much so, in fact, that when you meet people with similar opinions you tend to band together; because you agree with each other it's easier to get on. So, when a willing receptacle comes along in the form of a child, you tend to pour your beliefs into it. Whatever you express as a belief to the child starts to influence what the child believes. Look around you," he nods gently, indicating the people sharing our space. "All of the people in this coffee shop will have been fed ideas and beliefs as children by the adults around them. And many of them will have ended up agreeing with some of those ideas and beliefs because, over time, they were reinforced by other adults around them."

"Right..." I interject to show I am paying attention, but signalling that I need more.

"The child learns to conform to the society it is brought up in, the ideas and beliefs it experiences as it grows up. For the most part, the child makes an agreement with the adults around them that their ideas and beliefs are right. So it is possible, in time, for the child to become a reflection of what the adults around it have offered."

"OK," I say, just about following his line of thought.

"So strong is this that it can influence ideas, thought and beliefs about the self."

"Keep going," I'm gripped and distantly aware that even my stomach muscles are tensing in anticipation.

"As the child grows older it gains independence and expresses free thought. However, by *that* time it is possible that beliefs about the self have already become deep rooted; some patterns of belief are already set and are being acted out of without question. If a child grows up without the freedom to question or challenge, it is less likely to question or challenge some of these ingrained beliefs as an adult."

This is new thinking for me and not easy to hear. It seems that, as a parent, he is saying that I have been influencing Emily according to my own beliefs. I'm not sure I like what I'm hearing. I don't know how to respond, but I'd really like to know more, "Go on."

"This is the responsibility I refer to adults having. To be aware that they are laying down beliefs which children pick up and formulate as their own. The responsibility of the parent or adult is to allow the child to arrive at its own decisions based on its own thinking. By all means steer and protect the child, as any adult would do, especially morally, but be willing to allow the child to develop and question its own beliefs based on its own experiences and thoughts."

"OK, so I think I've got the idea now; what you're saying is that, even without intending to, we influence children according to the beliefs we have."

"Yes."

"But... Excuse me, Gabriel; why are we talking about this? What has this got to do with me?"

"While you acquire beliefs about yourself based on the experiences you have, even as an adult; there are many beliefs you will have arrived at on an unconscious level in the early years of your life. I want you to become more aware of the agreements you have made with yourself, the beliefs you have about yourself. It may be that some of your beliefs are so strong they are getting in the way of you being able to create change. Imagine for a moment, it were possible to make a fresh agreement with yourself about who you are and what you are capable of?" he leaves a silence as if he's waiting for me to grasp the importance of what he's just said. "Remember, your mind has the ability to change. Agreements become beliefs; and because you have the ability to change your mind, you can change the agreements you make with yourself. Choose to change those agreements and you free the possibility of new beliefs, about yourself and how you live. Different versions of you are allowed the possibility of being released."

"So you're not commenting on what I've done with Emily then? You're not suggesting that I do anything different?"

"That is for you to work out, Tom, not I. I am only here to raise your self awareness."

I relax a little as my initial fear that he is pointing a finger at me wanes. He is talking about what has influenced *me*. I guess I must have been influenced by those around me, and 'yes' I suppose I have agreed with a lot of the beliefs I've been offered as I grew up. I take a deep breath in as this idea settles with me. "So, it's up to me to choose change? Is that what you're saying?"

"Yes. You always have options in your life and in any moment you have a choice on which option to go for. It's the decision you make on which option you choose that determines the future you create; the reality of how things are."

"But do I really make such decisions all the time?" I ask.

"Yes. You decided to make that call on your mobile phone while driving, for instance. There were other options available to you, but, because of absorbed, practised and embedded beliefs and patterns of behaviour, you chose that one, in that moment. That choice, that decision, led directly to you being here."

I shake my head in disbelief at my own stupidity. "I guess you're right!" Then recognise that at least I was able to meet Gabriel. "Hey, I suppose every cloud has a silver lining!"

He nods a smile at me across the table and sits back in his sofa. "That choice is a clear example of what we're talking about. Yet again, this comes down to awareness, Tom. Unless you are aware of the agreements you make with yourself they have the potential to manipulate and manoeuvre you. As you know, some decisions are made on an unconscious level, so becoming aware of them can be difficult. At a deeper level, this is about tuning in to the effect unconscious dialogue can have on your belief system. But being willing to raise your awareness allows you to question why you think and behave in certain ways and affords you the ability, and opportunity, to create change. Otherwise you allow your agreements and beliefs the potential to manipulate you. We've already identified how powerful belief is in being able to move forward; but it is also possible for a belief to hold you back, like the anchor holding the boat back. Sometimes, in order to move forward, you need to let go of certain beliefs; the ones that get in the way."

This is all well and good for Gabriel to say, but it leaves me with another question. "If I don't know about a belief because it's come from an unconscious agreement, then how can I let go of it?"

"By listening and noticing more," he says, as if it were the most logical thing to come next.

"What does that mean?" I ask, frustrated at yet another new idea.

"I think it's fair to say that you understand the importance of awareness, isn't it?" I nod back at him. "Well, let's take it a step further. Awareness is about *listening* to the dialogue you have with yourself, and it's about *noticing* how you behave and respond. Listen to the internal and notice the external."

"I see," I say, picking up the essence of the idea, but still not sure how this helps me.

"Though the internal and external may appear separate they are linked; in essence, what happens in your mind influences how you behave. By paying attention, by listening and noticing more, you start to recognise agreements and beliefs being acted out through your behaviours. Some of these behaviours are so well practised and established that they have become the patterns we talked about before; patterns of behaviour set by the agreements you have made with yourself about who you are and how you do things. Once you notice these, you can name them as behaviours and start to recognise them being acted out. And once you notice this you open up the possibility of being able to trace backwards, to identify the beliefs that drive such behaviours. That is what I mean by listening and noticing more.

"With this level of awareness you can either notice yourself about to act out a particular behaviour or notice a belief coming in to play before the behaviour is enacted. At either of these points you can then question if that belief and behaviour are supportive of the best way forward for you at that time.

"You obviously believed it was acceptable for you to have that specific conversation on your mobile phone while you were driving in those conditions; your pattern of behaviour was so well established that you just did it."

"You're going to keep bringing that up aren't you? I say, my sense of shame and foolishness lending a resentful edge to my voice.

"You did ask how to change something when it is an unconscious way for you. Well, this is the answer. Would you say that it's an example of an unconscious belief being enacted?"

I struggle to answer him as, to be honest, I really have no idea about the processes involved; it's just what I do. "Yeah," I shrug my shoulders. "I guess it is. It's something I do without thinking about."

"That is exactly why I brought it up. If you start to hear your beliefs as they come up or notice the behaviours as you enact them, or are about to enact them, you can ask if they are the best for you at that time; and from that point you open the possibility of applying a different approach and release the possibility of a different outcome.

"Once you are aware of something you have a choice: carry on doing the same or choose to do something different. Bearing in mind that if you carry on doing the same, you are likely to generate the same outcome; whereas, doing something different opens up the possibility of change. And that all comes about as a result of listening and noticing more."

Gosh, he really has taken the gloves off this time. He just landed the perfect punch to get his point across. But, given that I asked the question, I had better hear the answer even if it comes across as quite hard work. "Wouldn't I run the risk of becoming somewhat introspective by doing all this though?" I ask.

"That's an understandable point of view, given that this is new to you. But then a lot of what I've been talking to you about has been new. Yet you seem to not only have accepted them, you actually refer to them as we speak."

"Yes, you're right, again," I concede

"This isn't about listening for and noticing everything, Tom. In fact many of your beliefs and ways of being will be fine. But if you notice something getting in the way of you moving forward, then perhaps it's time to pay more attention to what's driving it. I prefer to think of it as being more involved. It's about tuning in and filtering for what's useful, knowing when to pay attention and when not. Deciding what's worth keeping and what's worth changing. It all comes back to being aware," he says, with one of his slightly wry looks.

"And this is all part of thinking differently?" I ask, trying to connect this with what we've previously discussed.

"Yes. By becoming aware of your internal dialogue and the concept of choice, you raise the possibility of having a different dialogue and altering your beliefs. And this is where the conversation on children becomes most relevant. If you are not aware of the agreements you have made with yourself then how can you change them? Many of the agreements made in a child's formative years are formed on an unconscious level. People are simply not aware of them and so many patterns of being and doing have come about as a result of passive choices."

"But does that mean that all unconscious agreements are made in childhood?" I ask.

"No, you make unconscious agreements with yourself all the time; some come out of instinct and some are emotionally driven. The art lies in being able to recognise them as they surface, as the agreement manifests itself in a conscious thought, a way of behaving, how you sound and what you say. Look around you. The people here are a result of what they have experienced to date and the agreements they have made with themselves. If they want to create change they must *choose* to change; choose to make some new agreements with themselves."

"That harsh, Gabriel," I suddenly feel defensive for everyone who hasn't met him. "These people aren't aware of what you have been telling me, you can't blame them for being how they are."

"There you go, talking about blame again. No one is being

blamed here. There is no judgement on these people for living their lives the way they do. Being here," he opens his arms to indicate the coffee shop, "merely serves to highlight that most people are unaware of what you and I are talking about. It is also fair to say though, without blame, that these people are *choosing* to live the way they do. But given that several factors influencing them are embedded at an early age; most are unaware of them and are therefore unaware that they act out of them from day to day."

"It sounds like you're saying that a lot of these agreements are wrong," I say, pretty sure that's what I'm hearing.

"Not at all. I merely raise the question of how you think in relation to yourself and what you have become accustomed to. A lot of the agreements you make with yourself are completely appropriate for where you are in your life at that time. Again, Tom, there is no judgement on that; if you choose to carry on with such agreements that's fine, so long as you do so on a conscious level. Be aware of your thoughts and your beliefs; become more conscious of yourself, of how you are.

"I am talking about stepping outside of limiting beliefs and discovering new possibilities. By opening your mind to the potential for new possibilities you increase the likelihood of stepping beyond a version of you which you may have become accustomed to and comfortable with. Be willing to break agreements you have previously made with yourself. Have a different dialogue with yourself; make some new agreements. Either carry on as you are and do nothing to change and accept the consequences of that; or decide to make it be different. But only you can make that choice," he says, his eyes pierce me as keenly as the sincerity of his words.

As I think through his latest offering I lift my cup for another sip of coffee, but on finding it now cold I disappointedly place it back on the table without drinking any. "So being passionate and believing isn't enough then?"

"Is there something wrong with your coffee?" he asks.

His change of subject catches me out. I hadn't thought what I'd done with the coffee was that noticeable. "Oh, no, it's just gone cold, that's all."

"In that moment you wanted some coffee, yet you chose not to drink any because it was not how you like it. At some point in the past you made an agreement with yourself that you don't like cold coffee. Yet other people drink cold coffee, because they choose to like it. So, on this occasion, you chose not to drink that which was perfectly drinkable. That was an unconscious agreement being played out right there. Try it now," he says, nodding towards my mug.

I'm about to say 'No thanks', but as I look down I'm surprised to see that the mug is once again brimming with cocoa-covered froth. I look back at Gabriel, beaming a bemused smile, before reaching down to pick the mug up. "Thanks," I smell the fresh brew. "That first one was just how I like it."

He smiles back at me, "You choose to do things or not do them all the time, Tom. It's the choices you make that determine what you get back. Your future is made by the choices you make from moment to moment."

"Do we really make choices like this all the time though?" I ask again and place the mug back on the table having taken a sip of the fresh hot coffee.

"Yes, you do. Moment by moment your future is created by the choices you make; some you are aware of, some unaware. And there's a *grey* area in between."

"Oh, why I am I not surprised there's a grey area? Go on then, explain that one to me."

"The grey area is where you choose not to recognise or give value to something you actually have a level of awareness of. Where you are aware of something but choose to ignore its impact on you, maybe you don't recognise its worth, or you deny its relevance to you. Some people hide in this grey area," he says, holding my gaze with a moment of silence. "They make choices from a position of denial."

"Give me an example of this would you please? I'm not sure I fully understand."

He looks around. "Right; see that lady over there, by the window, the blonde lady with the brown blouse and two children sitting opposite her?"

I look over to where he's indicating, I see a lady with her hair pulled loosely back in a pony tail; a mug in both her hands. Her two children are squabbling and pushing each other, but she's looking out of the window having seemingly mastered the ability to tune out their bickering rivalry. "Yeah, I see her; the one taking a drink from her mug?"

"That's the one. She has been a smoker for eighteen years, but she wants to stop. She recognises that smoking is bad for her health and she also understands that it's costing her money, money that could buy the children clothes and toys. She even says in conversation how she thinks it would be a good idea to stop smoking. Yet she does nothing to stop. It could be said that she is making an informed choice to smoke, because she is *aware* of the drawbacks. Now, when it comes to methods for stopping, she avoids them. She says they are too expensive, or she calls them too 'weird' for her; she even says she is *incapable* of stopping, she says she does not have the will-power. All of these are excuses. She wants to stop and she is aware of methods that are available to help her do this. However, she is choosing to ignore the real possibility that she could stop. So, she carries on, in that grey area, talking about stopping but not being willing to do what it takes. If you said to her that she freely chooses to smoke, given that she knows solutions and help are available, she would probably say that she really wants to stop; but then all the excuses would come as to why she can't. So she is operating in the grey area, in denial.

"Many people avoid committing to creating change that could transform their lives. They bury their head in sand when solutions are available, rather than resolve money issues, love problems, dissatisfaction at work, and a whole host of things."

I turn back to face him and his eyes come back from looking at the lady to meet mine. "Am I like that?" I ask.

"Many of people in this room are like that, Tom. You are no different to them, or should I say, you *were* no different. Your level of awareness is far better now though; you have been given the chance to recognise how you were and, more importantly, you are being given the opportunity to create things being different. You are being offered the chance to choose change. Choice determines who you are and what you have. Choice is one of your greatest gifts, and it is the extent to which you are prepared to compromise yourself in losing or giving away your choice that determines the extent to which you experience freedom." He holds my eyes again when he stops speaking. In that moment it feels like he is holding time still; except that, all around me, life in the coffee shop carries on as normal. I feel incapable of speaking, suspended for what seems like minutes before he speaks again. "You make many choices in your life and the choices you make define who you are. Having looked at the truth of what has led to you being who you are, experiencing what you have in your life, here is your choice – if you were to go back would you accept and be satisfied with that truth or would you choose a new way?"

The room might be active, people might be speaking, but I may as well be in an empty box with him. Nothing else matters. Even the smell of coffee caressing my nostrils vanishes. As the seconds tick by I find I can't even blink. My breathing becomes shallow and my heart beats slower. Then Gabriel's soft voice touches my ears once again. "Whichever you choose is fine, Tom. Whatever you choose, ultimately it is your choice. If you choose to make no changes, you will not be judged. You will still be with me until it is time for you to go to your next destination, wherever it may be; we will still meet and talk until it is time for you to go. If you choose for your life to be as it was before, I will accept your choice, though I will still talk to you about your options, for that is in my nature and the reason I am here. But if you choose to change it will inform how we are and what we talk about in the future. This is just one moment of choice; there will be others. It is rather like a junction in the road, where you can take the left fork or the right fork. But whichever one you take you will be different because of the time you've spent with me. Whichever you choose, you will move forward. You can look back but you cannot go backwards. You are always moving forward, Tom, and the choices you make influence what you create."

"But what if I choose to not make any changes, Gabriel?" I enquire.

He considers his response for a moment. "If I can be honest with you, Tom; I'd be surprised. Because you have given me plenty of indications that you would like to change things. However," he lifts his tone, "if you choose to keep things as they are, that is your choice and I will respect that. With one exception."

I dip my head sideways, grabbed by his somewhat dramatic shift. "Go on."

"If you choose to accept your life being the way it has been without change then you must do so graciously."

"What does that mean?" I ask.

"If you choose to accept things as they were, you must learn to accept *that* life, fully. Which means accepting everything life gives you in that state; not complaining about your lot, about what you have or have not, no wishing for anything different. Full and unequivocal acceptance of everything you have in that life. Accept what you have. If you feel a need to complain or feel bad about what you have, it will be plain to me that you are not happy with your choice and I will talk to you about that. It might also mean that we need to revisit some of the areas we have already been looking at and discussing. If you show dissatisfaction, it is likely that you will have chosen from a state of denial about something."

The entire conversation with Gabriel in the coffee shop now makes sense. All the different areas we had been discussing since we met come together. I sit back in my chair, Gabriel's eyes keeping me safe in our shared world; then I tear my eyes away to look around the room and in that instant the room appears to spring back into life. I look at the lady with the brown blouse. I look at the business men in their suits as they pore over a laptop intently. I look at the young couple so obviously in love, sharing a world that only exists between themselves. I look at the line of people queuing to be served, some patiently waiting, some eager to buy and move on somewhere else, the old ladies looking round purposefully for where they can sit to enjoy their coffee and chat. Then a fresh thought brings me back to Gabriel. "You know?" I say. "I think I know my answer on this one, Gabriel, but can I share something with you?"

"I'm listening," he says, not altering his comfortable reclined pose.

"This may sound strange, given that I make so many decisions at work, decisions that involve significant sums of money and influence a lot of people; but the truth is that I can find making personal decisions quite hard. Sometimes I just wish there was someone who could help me make the decisions or even make them *for* me," I finish with a slight chuckle, acknowledging how bizarre it is for me to admit this.

"Discussing things with other people makes sense. It is good to get others opinions; you probably find it helps you to make your mind up. In fact, there are many advantages to talking things over with other people."

"Yeah, well, that's not something I've been particularly good at," I admit.

"In that case, what have you been doing?"

"Mostly mulling things over in my head. Doing it by myself I suppose."

"Getting thoughts out of your head is a very good idea, Tom. Trying to maintain order in a space where many voices of opinion are competing can be difficult. Remember the idea of spin?" he asks.

"Ah, yes," I recognise that that is exactly what happens with me. My head gets so busy with thoughts whirring around sometimes that it is hard to single them out and make sense of them.

"Slowing down the rate at which your mind spins will undoubtedly help you in such situations, as it allows you to create clearer thoughts. But sharing those thoughts with others will also help you to crystallise them so they can be understood. Expressing your thoughts allows you to see the reality of them, to establish their worth. And by releasing your thoughts you free your mind to accommodate new ideas and perspectives."

"I'm just not good at doing that, I admit."

"Well, Tom, there is a first time for everything. What is the saying? 'A problem shared is a problem halved.' I can offer you this assurance though; if you keep doing what you have been doing, the outcomes will more than likely stay the same. It is time for you to start thinking differently; both about who you are and how you do things. Talk things over with people, and if you can't, then get it out of your head onto a sheet of paper. Things tend to become clearer and often appear simpler."

"Hmm…" I contemplate his ideas, realising that maybe it is time for some changes. Not only in how I live my life, but also in how I am. "I'd like to try that," I admit, "It'll feel uncomfortable, but I'd like to try it."

"Good. But there is one important thing for you to bear in mind," he says, enticingly. "One thing will never change… When it comes to decisions about you… You are the only one who can make such decisions. No one else can make them for you."

"Ain't that just the truth?" No matter how much I try to avoid it, at the end of the day, it's only ever just me who can choose which option to go for. Sometimes I get it right and sometimes I get it wrong.

"It is all right to change your mind," he says, as if he realises my concern. I look up at him quizzically. "It is all right to choose one thing and then realise it was not the best option for you. That's the beauty of choice; you have every right to change your mind, because you have freedom of choice. If you commit to your decision and back it fully, then subsequently realise it was not the best choice for you, then that is fine. Be humble and accept the reality of that moment; then you are free to consider the options ahead of you. Be in the moment, accept what comes and choose your way."

"Yeah, but other people tend to make judgements on us if we change our minds, don't they? So being seen as someone who makes clear and accurate decisions is important to me," I say.

"We've talked about this before. It seems to me you're more concerned about what other people think, Tom," he says. "Look, if you make a decision then realise it wasn't the best, for you or for others, then it would seem appropriate to change your mind based on what you now know. Making the initial decision allowed you to move in a specific direction which revealed what that direction had to offer. From that moment on you have new information to help you assess and make fresh decisions. Of course you make mistakes; it is part of being human," he says with a slight laugh. "You can't foretell the future, you cannot know if every decision you make will be right, and as time moves on what may have felt right in one moment can feel different in another moment. How you are in recognising those moments and how you respond makes a difference. If you can be gracious in acknowledging that something which once felt right now feels wrong and respond humbly when changing your mind, that is the sign of a strong person. In those moments, if you are gracious and humble, if you are respectful of other people and considerate of the impact on others when making changes, then it should not matter what other people think."

"I guess you're right," I say, leaning forward to take a sip of my coffee.

"Thank you," he replies. I notice a distinctly cheeky air about him as I slowly savour my cappuccino. "So, what is it to be? Which fork in the road will you choose in this moment?" His perfect poise and relaxed manner completely at odds with the feeling balling up in my stomach.

Even though I have no idea what is ahead of me, I am nervous of making a commitment. "Is it really time to make a choice?" I say.

"The future is made by the choices made from moment to moment, Tom."

I lower the mug away from my lips slowly, hovering it at chin height, "Gosh, it's surprising how when the moment comes I find myself feeling so nervous."

"What are you afraid of?" he asks calmly.

My eyes flit around aimlessly tracing the coffee table ahead of me, "I don't know!"

"Fear is in the imagination."

"Hmm!" I mutter, pulling away from my thoughts to look up at him.

"Fear takes place in the mind; and the mind will try to protect you. It will try to stop you from breaking away from what it has become accustomed to and feels safe with. But, remember, resting between the dream of doing and the fear of failure lie the pieces of the possible. Think about what you want and what you believe is good for you."

Again the room disappears from my consciousness; even though there is movement and sound all around I can see or hear none of it. My heart thumps at the walls of my chest and I feel more alive than I have in years.

"It's all right, Tom. It's all right to feel as you do. Strange how you can feel so alive while actually in a coma," he says, making it sound like a joke.

"Yeah!" I whisper loudly, still holding the mug by my chin, transfixed.

"In this moment you are responding from a state you've become used to. You are used to steering away from uncomfortable situations, to protecting yourself. You are programmed to avoid confrontation, to steer away from conflict and to seek out safe places; this is part of your survival mechanism. In moments when you sense a threat to stability, your mind and body act out of a reflex to protect you. Remind me, what was it you did when you saw the car on the road ahead of you before the crash, Tom?"

Flashes of the accident flicker in my mind as I recall that moment. "I slammed the brakes on," I say.

"And what else?"

I play back the moment just before the collision, "I tried to avoid hitting the car, but failed," I say, unsure of what else to say.

"Exactly, you tried to steer out of danger; it was an instinctive reaction to have. In that instance it was the appropriate action to take; even though it didn't stop the eventual outcome. But that instinctive desire for safety is so highly attuned that it tends to steer you away from any situation you perceive as uncomfortable or dangerous. Hence, when faced with making decisions that you think will be difficult your desire to steer away is powerful; you want to avoid the issue. That is what is happening now. You are trying to steer away, aren't you?"

"Yes," I hadn't realised it initially, but Gabriel pointing it out has made it obvious to me.

"Sometimes the best way forward is to steer in the direction of your discomfort; to face up to that which is daunting you, that which you feel uncomfortable about. Only by being willing to go in the direction of your discomfort do you open up the possibility of a different outcome to that which you tend to repeat. Now, in many cases where your instinct is to steer away, it is an appropriate response to help avoid the threat. However, there are occasions when you encounter something which you perceive as a threat, but which is actually nothing more than discomfort. Your survival mechanism kicks in to help you feel safe, but actually, by steering out of the situation, you may only be postponing it or steering towards greater trouble further down the road. Sometimes, the best solution is to steer into your discomfort and address the thing which makes you feel uncomfortable. Change can be uncomfortable, so your mind and body will send instructions to steer away. The question is, if you've been doing the same things over and over beforehand and by doing so you ended up here; is it time for a change? Only by doing something different can you expect to create a different outcome or have a different experience." He holds my eyes once more in a moment that defines exactly why I am here with him, having these conversations.

I take a sip of coffee, its warmth filtering deep into me; then another. My eyes search upwards, picturing my life as it has been, floating moments across my mind like the images that had come to me when I first met Gabriel. Then my eyes drop down as emotion after emotion plays out like a symphony inside me. I realise the time has come to change how I approach my life. Where I'd felt nervous only moments before, I am now light inside, almost as if I've let go of a great burden that has been keeping me emotionally weighed down. My heartbeat slows and a sense of happiness glows from the pit of my stomach, growing to fill my heart and head as I lift my eyes once more to look across the table at Gabriel. Since we first met, we have shared many moments this way, our eyes creating an inextricable bond between us; but none have been quite like this one. This moment defines the essence of my pause time; everything else in my consciousness has disappeared. Time truly is on hold as he embraces and protects me in what I can only describe as a cocoon of peace. I hear nothing from him, not aloud and not directly to my mind, but I sense a message conveying 'I accept you.'

In that moment any pretence I have been previously harbouring disappears. I am more naked than ever before in my life. It feels as if I am being seen as never before. Whoever I was and whatever I may have previously done is being accepted. This moment is the embodiment of what Gabriel has been saying; there is no sense of judgement or blame at all. I am being seen and accepted for who I am. Whatever may have happened in my life prior to meeting Gabriel pales into insignificance. Through the silence and stillness I am sharing with him I hear a voice say 'It's OK'. But I don't recognise this voice. It certainly isn't Gabriel's and, given that I am completely disconnected from anything happening around me, it isn't coming from anyone in the coffee shop. As I hear the words resonate, I realise the voice is coming from inside me. The voice and words are my own. I listen for more; all the while Gabriel looks across at me, supporting me as if he knows what's happening.

Then the voice clearly but softly speaks, 'It's all right to let go'. This time I not only hear the voice, I feel it. A sense of being light comes over me, like I can float; my whole body begins to droop as if I am letting go of each part of my being. Everything starts to pale around me, just as when previous scenes disappeared before my eyes. My back curves as my shoulders round, my tummy falls inwards and my head drops. My eyes close as I breathe, slowly, calmly, deeply in. As much as I might still want to go back to live, I recognise it is time for me to let go of that need and open up to whatever other possibility might lie ahead of me. An immense sense of peace comes over me. A sense I can only describe as ultimate acceptance. Acceptance of my fate. It is all right to let go.

My body relaxes, just as when a general anaesthetic is taking hold of me before surgery. "Your time has come, Tom," I hear Gabriel's warm voice say. "It is time to leave me."

"But where am I going?" I hear myself say as the whiteness closes in, working its way inside me.

"You are going back," his distant voice says. He's far away from me now, as the whiteness becomes complete, all around and inside me.

Silence.

A Fresh Start

I hear a faint electronic beat, becoming clearer and sharper, dragging me from the depths of a heavy sleep.

I try to swallow but struggle. My throat is constricted and won't allow me to gulp.

The beat pulses steadily like a metronome.

I open my eyes and see a stark ceiling above and what looks like the track for a curtain around a hospital bed. Am I in a hospital? If so, why's he brought me to a hospital? Then a flicker of hope dashes through me; am a back in the land of the living? Am I alive?

I start to look around, but find it hard to move. I'm surprisingly stiff, until I realise that physically I may not have actually moved for a long time and, is this pain I'm feeling?

I'm alive!

Yes, this is the curtain track above my bed, and the curtain is pulled back to the side of the bed. There is the wooden armed visitors chair at my bedside; a copy of Captain Corelli's Mandolin spread open and face down on its seat. Beyond that I see a window revealing a cloudy grey day outside. Who cares what the weather is like, I am alive! In turning to look at the other side I see that I must be in a private room as there are no other beds. There are two internal windows; one ahead of me, looking onto an empty corridor; the other with an open door next to it, leading to a bay with desks and chairs, and charts on the wall above. All I can make out on the charts is a grid marked up in hand written black ink. No one is around. Please don't make this another one of Gabriel's locations for another chat. But where is he? Where is anyone?

I try to move my right arm and notice that it is in a cast; I'm incapable of moving it. I try to move my legs and can't move them either. Am I paralysed? Oh no, Gabriel has been preparing me for this!

The electronic beat picks up pace. It must be my heart monitor reflecting the state of panic seeping in to me. Out of nowhere a young nurse comes rushing through the open door and stops still looking at me, a smile growing across her face. "Mr Patterson. You're awake."

The heart monitor is beeping faster now. I open my mouth to speak, but no sound comes out. My mouth and throat are dry and what comes up is merely a heavy breath sound caught in the back of my throat. I swallow hard, painfully.

"It's alright Mr Patterson. You've been in a coma. I'm Angela, your nurse. Don't try to speak just yet. Let me get you some water," she says.

I try to say 'yes', but again, the sound catches in my throat. I nod, my eyes blinking uncomfortably. The heart monitor's rhythm settles back in to a slower pace.

From the bedside unit she pours me a small glass of water but leaves it on the side as she picks up a remote control clipped to the side of my bed. She pushes one of its buttons and the top half of me rises until I am sitting up in bed. She gently places a hand around my neck and head and brings the glass up to my lips. I take a sip of water. The cool refreshing liquid soothes my mouth and throat as it searches its way down inside me. "It's good to see you awake," she says. I turn to her and mouth the word 'thanks' with just enough air to make a sound out of it. I look down and see a blanket over my legs, which look bulkier underneath. I try to move them again, but can only feel my buttocks and the top most part of my legs responding at all. I look back at the nurse, expressing as much concern as I am able through my eyes, with a quick glance back towards my legs. "You were in an accident, Mr Patterson; both your legs were badly broken. You'll probably have to learn how to walk again." Are nurses taught this soft tone or does it just come naturally for them?

I look back at my legs. That explains the bulk, they must be in casts. I guess I should consider myself lucky. Not only am I alive, but my legs are only broken; I'm not paralysed. I drop my head back into the pillow supporting me. Was that someone at the window ahead of me looking through into my room? I lift my head again to see and make out the figure of my mum looking in through the window, holding a cardboard cup in her hand. She looks exhausted and drawn and as her eyes meet mine; she's clearly as caught out as I am by this moment. A slow smile makes its way across my face as tears well in my eyes and that lump appears back in my throat.

She walks towards the entrance to my room, and as she does I see someone has been standing behind her. Gabriel. He moves up to the window and raises a clipboard so it is facing in to my room. There is a piece of paper attached with three words written large and bold.

> *Choose*
> *your*
> *way*

He gives me a big warm smile, lifts a hand, waves and is then gone. He disappears, just like the images he'd taken me to see.

Mum walks in through the door and stops still, looking at me, a smile emerging through tear filled eyes.

Distilled principles

For those of you who prefer overview descriptions I have distilled the books key principles for quick reference.

Awareness

Become aware of the factors that have lead to you being who you are having what you have right now; what I refer to as the 'truth of your today'.

Notice what has influenced you over the years and how you have responded to what came your way.

Like it or not, all your actions, all you have said and done has lead you to this point. All that has come your way has had an influence; if not directly then in how you have responded to such events.

Notice the choices you made at crucial moments in the past; all these have lead to the truth of your today. The thoughts you have and your ways of being, your responses and reactions, your successes and failures have all contributed to the truth of your today.

Acceptance

Acceptance does not mean you have to like or approve of the factors that have influenced and created who you are and what you have. Acceptance means just that: accept that these factors are what have lead to the truth of your today.

Becoming aware of and taking responsibility for your patterns of thought, behaviours and responses is crucial to being able to let go of them. You do not need to defend or be proud in order to accept; acceptance is quite simply the process of coming to terms with the truth of the past and of today.

As much as it's about taking responsibility for the part you played in creating what you have, it is equally about accepting the things you can't take responsibility for, but which have influenced you. External factors influence you and, while you can't accept responsibility for them happening as they were beyond your control, you can accept and take responsibility for how you responded to them.

Accept what has happened, how you responded and the part you played in creating the truth of your today.

Desire

It could all stop at accepting the truth of your today, nothing *has* to change; at least you would be conscious of the part you've played in creating that truth. You may be happy being at this level of consciousness. However, if you would like to change an aspect of how things are, now is the time to change the patterns of behaviour and habituated responses that reinforce things being as they are; and the best way to increase your chances of making that happen is to truly want the change, to desire the difference.

Too many people talk about wanting aspects of their life to be different but do little to actually make it happen. Desire the difference and internally a shift takes place that frees you to commit to making the change happen. I'm not saying that it will magically occur, but it is fair to say that when you desire something you commit to achieving that which you desire, to doing what it takes to make it happen and, as a result, your ability to overcome obstacles increases dramatically.

Believe

For those of you who have read Pieces of the Possible you will know that the 'belief' I refer to is not that of religious faith; it's about a thought that becomes so strong that it is believed in. There is plenty evidence to prove that when we believe something it informs the language we use and the patterns of behaviour we enact in pursuing that which we believe.

You will help yourself invaluably if you believe:
- Things can be different
- You deserve the change (it is right or appropriate for you)
- The change is realistic and achievable
- You are going to make the change happen
- You can let go of old ways of thinking and patterns of behaviour
- Obstacles and resistance from others are not going to stop you

There may be other things, personal to you, that you might need to create belief around; but be assured that these beliefs will help you achieve your desired change.

Let go

Now you are on the journey to creating change; but beware, because old patterns of thinking and behaviour are powerful, and familiarity or comfort with them will attempt to pull you back.

To prove how powerful old patterns are try this: make a categorical change to the location of the waste bin in your kitchen and notice just how many times you will be caught out when you physically go straight to where the bin had previously been located. It takes time for change to settle and to overcome familiarity or comfort with old patterns.

Letting go of old patterns takes effort and commitment to new ways. But it isn't just about letting go of old patterns, it's also about letting go of 'old you' and the comfort that comes with 'old you'. 'Old you' will try hard to pull you back. People's familiarity with 'old you' will encourage them to try and pull you back to old ways. The effort involved in sticking to a clear vision of a different future can take its toll and the draw of 'old you' will seem very attractive. In order to move on you need to let go of old patterns, of old familiarity and 'old you'. How you were is not how you are now. How you did things is not how you do things now.

It may be that there are things you need to say 'goodbye' to, to release or to mourn going. However you choose to do that is up to you, but let go of them you must in order to welcome change.

Choose it

The future is created by the choices you make from moment to moment. You have a multitude of different versions inside and different possible futures awaiting you, all released by how you choose to respond to what you experience moment to moment.

Each fork in the road offers different options; the fork you choose establishes a new route and sets in place the possibility of a different future. Make this choice a consciously, clearly defined moment that sets you out with the first step along a new route. Choose it, believe it, enact it.

You will encounter challenges, old patterns will appear very attractive, commitment will be doubted; but if you stay true to the principles laid out here you increase the likelihood of creating the change you desire.

This is not just a book to me, it's a way of life, enabling me to keep growing and adapt how I engage with the world. But because

I am human, I make mistakes and I stray from the principles; the difference is I keep re-connecting with them and re-committing to make changes that will benefit me.

If you're interested in attending 'Choose to Change', the personal growth programme I run, please contact me on office@mtwtraining.com or via the More Than Words Training website www.mtwtraining.com.

I wish you the very best in the pursuit of your desired change.

Remember:
Resting between the dream of doing and the fear of failure lie the pieces of the possible.